The Soul of the Universe

The Soul of the

UNIVERSE

———

GUSTAF STRÖMBERG

———

PHILADELPHIA

David McKay Company

Washington Square

Dedicated

to

Professor John Elof Boodin

*The great thinker, historian, poet,
and philosopher*

FROM THE *turmoil caused by the great discoveries in the science of physics during the last decades two outstanding new principles have emerged. The first is contained in the Quantum Theory and explains the strange fact that both matter and light appear sometimes as particles and sometimes as waves. The second has evolved from the Theory of Relativity and has resulted in a realization that the material universe is a uniform and interrelated whole, that it is a special aspect of a rational Cosmos. These two new principles have in this book been applied to the field of biology and have been found extremely useful in explaining the marvelous structures and the purposeful organization in the living world. We can then understand how an egg cell can develop into an animal, and a larva into a butterfly, new light is thrown on the origin and the development of life on the earth, and as in a flash we realize the meaning and nature of death.*

The two principles have also been applied to the age-old problem of the relationship between mind and matter. We can then understand the connection between the chemical and electric processes in the nervous system and the corresponding sensations and feelings. The most startling results of this study are that the individual memory is probably indestructible and that the essence of all living elements is probably immortal. The study leads to the inevitable conclusion that there exists a World Soul or God.

Contents

Preface

IN DAYS of extreme specialization in science the appearance of a well-considered book which brings together many of the facts and conceptions of different branches of physical and biological science and discusses them from a unified and philosophical point of view is exceedingly welcome. Very often the specialist immersed in his own field of research has a very limited outlook and but little interest in the broader aspects of science or in its applications to human life and behavior.

Dr. Gustaf Strömberg was born in Sweden and received his scientific training in mathematics, physics and celestial mechanics in the admirable universities of that country. He came to the Mount Wilson Observatory of the Carnegie Institution of Washington in 1916 and has remained upon its staff since that time, becoming a naturalized citizen of the United States in 1922. At Mount Wilson he familiarized himself with the applications of physics, and especially of spectrum analysis, to astronomy, and has completed and published many investigations dealing with statistical problems relating to the motions and luminosities of the stars and the structure of the universe. He writes with full authority on subjects having to do with physics and physical astronomy.

The sections of this book devoted to the biological sciences have been based upon extensive reading and study by the author, supplemented by the advice and criticism of well-known authorities in the field. They should represent an accurate statement of the principal facts in a branch of knowledge which is developing with extraordinary rapidity.

The final chapters of Dr. Strömberg's book dealing with human behavior and man's intellectual and spiritual qualities will doubtless be judged in many different ways by different readers, and it is quite impossible to expect unanimity of opinion on these major problems of the human race. As a scientist with strong philosophical interests, however, the author brings to the discussion of these great questions resources of knowledge and understanding and a simplicity of statement which can hardly fail to arrest the attention and stimulate the thought and imagination of the intelligent reader.

WALTER S. ADAMS

Introduction

WE ARE starting on a journey of exploration. We intend to search for something the existence of which has been vaguely suspected by many thinkers. We shall search for the Soul of the Universe. It is an ambitious undertaking, nevertheless most of us have at some time or other been engaged in such a search. The search has gone on from the time human beings first began to ask serious questions about themselves and about the Nature they observe around them. They have wondered about the changes they see in stars, in inert matter, in plants and animals, and in their own bodies. They have tried to study the mysteries of consciousness itself, how the signals from the outside world are transmitted and modified before they appear as sensations, pictures, and ideas in an individual being, why we act in different ways under similar conditions, whether we are really free to do what we want, and what are the limits of our knowledge and our powers. The most important question asked by man is the meaning of it all, and in particular the meaning of human life. Am I a piece of matter like a stone governed solely by blind and seemingly cruel forces, and is it only a question of chance whether I am happy or unhappy, whether I live or die? Is my life like a wave in the ocean, which rises and falls and disappears and is replaced by another, or is there anything left of my personality after I am dead and forgotten? Was I only a link between generations to be discarded as useless, when my time was up, or had my earthly life a deeper significance? If I caused suffering among my fellow-men and if I took their property and life to further my own interests or those of my family, nation, or race, was that a good or a bad or an indifferent act from the point of view of eternity? Is there a higher entity than man in the universe and how can we find out anything about its existence and relationship to us?

Questions like these have been asked by all thinking men, and they have searched for the answers in Nature, within themselves, in wise men's sayings, and in old documents, regarded as inspired in some way or other. Some people put their faith in revelations, others give more weight to their own observations, experience, and logical reasoning, their attitude in this respect depending upon their temperament, environment, experience, and early training.

The study here presented is based mainly on facts from physics, biology, and physiology. The facts are well known to students, the new things lie in the emphasis, the viewpoints, and the interpretations. Even the most simple observation may lead to startling conclusions, if the analysis of it is carried far enough. Wrong conclusions will certainly be drawn in many instances, but honest attempts to find some answers are better than no attempts at all to penetrate into the Great Unknown of which we all are parts.

No attempt has been made to trace the history of the development of the conceptions of the universe, of matter, of life and of human behavior. Philosophy is almost as old as humanity, and the writer has no intention whatever of giving a history of philosophical thought. If the thoughts are important to us, it matters little if they were expressed by a recognized authority or not. We must ourselves judge whether we think opinions are correct or not, we do not willingly delegate this responsibility to some one else. He may without doubt be more capable of judging the evidence, but we are so vitally interested in many of these problems that we want to have something to say about them ourselves. The nature of the problems is such that even the best informed men differ about the proper interpretations; sometimes the details conceal the whole, prejudice distorts the view, the subjective nature of our perceptions is forgotten, and fear of ridicule prevents expression of unorthodox thoughts. Sometimes intuition, subconscious thoughts, or inspirations play important parts in forming the answers, the personal element is here more pronounced than in other kinds of study.

As often happens in scientific research, when we are looking for the answers to certain questions, unexpected things appear and answers are found to questions which originally were outside the field of investigation. The present study was first intended to cover the limited field of physics, but the subject matter seemed to have a life of its own, and it soon extended into many other fields of human knowledge. The writer let it grow freely, preserving, however, the logical connection between its parts.

The writer hopes that it may be of some value to those people who can think freely and without prejudice about the more important questions that confront mankind today. It may even bring renewed hope to many who have felt that materialistic science and nationalistic philosophies have destroyed the urge and incentive for moral development.

I am indebted to several people for help and encouragement during the preparation of this book. Since it contains much biology, and this science lies outside the field of research in which I am engaged, I was anxious to have the biological statements examined. My friend William D. Humason was kind enough to go through the first draft. Dr. Thomas Hunt Morgan, Professor of Biology at the California Institute of Technology, kindly offered to read the biological part and made several corrections in the description of biological facts. Dr. O. L. Sponsler, Professor of Botany at the University of California at Los Angeles, was kind enough to read the manuscript and made a few corrections. In the final rendering, however, several additions have been inserted after their scrutiny was made.

The manuscript has been submitted to several scientists interested in the philosophical implications of modern science. I am particularly indebted to Professor Albert Einstein for his encouragement and constructive criticism, which caused me to analyze more fully certain parts, to Sir Arthur Eddington, Dr. F. R. Moulton, Permanent Secretary of the American Association for the Advancement of Science, and to the Director of the Mount Wilson Observatory, Dr. Walter S. Adams, for their interest and encouragement. My friend Edward F. Adams of the Mount Wilson Observatory has been kind enough to read the manuscript and has suggested several improvements. It is a great pleasure to express here my appreciation for his help. I am also indebted to Mr. Boris de Zirkoff of Point Loma and Dr. Karel Hujer of Prague for the great interest they have taken in this work.

After the book was written I found that Dr. John Elof Boodin, Professor of Philosophy at the University of California at Los Angeles, in his many valuable books had made a historical and critical study of some of the problems discussed here. In his Cosmic Evolution and Three Interpretations of the Universe (Macmillan, 1925 and 1934) the reader will find a comprehensive survey of the history of the problems discussed. In his book GOD (Macmillan, 1934) another approach is described which is unsurpassed in its beauty and simplicity.

That these people have corrected some statements of fact or expressed interest and understanding of the ideas expressed does not, of course, mean that they have endorsed all my theories and conclusions. For the latter the writer is alone responsible.

Pasadena, California
   September, 1939

CHAPTER I

Space

I<small>N OUR</small> search for the Soul of the Universe we can
start anywhere. We could start with a study of
a drop of water, a tiny insect, the planet Earth or the
universe of stars. It makes no difference—they are
all *one*. Properly we should start with our own
consciousness, it is there we see the pictures of the
outside world, it is there we interpret our sensations
and formulate the laws of nature. In fact, the world
we describe exists in the first place within the consciousness of each individual and is, to a certain extent, a product of the same. We shall not start with
an analysis of what takes place in our consciousness,
that will come later. We shall begin with a study
of one of the most fundamental entities in the universe, *Space* itself.

Early men did not speculate about the subtle question of the nature of space. They were interested in
the things and the events in the nature around them.
They studied the properties of dead and living objects from the point of view of their usefulness as
food, clothing, tools, weapons or decorations; later
when their primary desires were satisfied they studied

the same objects more closely in order to satisfy a curiosity inborn in men. But space itself was elusive and intangible, to study it appeared as nonsensical as to study a realm of nothingness.

Space, like everything else, exists primarily in our consciousness, where it is most easily recognized as the property of apparent extension and separation of images. Its counterpart in the external world is called *physical space*. We are convinced that there exists a certain counterpart in the external world to our mental space, a conviction which has developed through a comparison of the simultaneous observations of many individuals. In our dreams we walk around in the private space of our own consciousness. In the science of physics, on the other hand, we describe the properties of a space which appears to be common to all human investigators.

We shall here study physical or external space, since for most people it appears more "real" than the space of our vision. How can we define or describe it? Jokingly, space has been described as what is left over when we take away all the matter, an expression which simply emphasizes the opinion that space is distinguished from matter and is not directly observable by our sense organs. In what way then can physical space reveal its existence, and what are its effects and properties?

In the first place physical space is associated with the number three, it has, as we say, *three dimensions*.

Bodies have extension in height, width and depth, the positions of points relative to one another are given by three numbers, when referred to a common system of reference. The intensity of light decreases with the *square* of the distance from the source, and this can be shown to be a consequence of the three-dimensional property of physical space. Mathematical physicists often describe natural phenomena as occurring in space and space-time of many dimensions, but this is an artifice used for special purposes and does not in any way imply that physical space can have anything but three dimensions.

In the phenomena of motion, space reveals itself as a tremendously powerful regulator. A railroad train is hurrying at excessive speed, guided in its motion by two straight tracks of steel. Nothing happens until it comes to a sharp turn, the train goes off the track, the cars tumble over and are bent and twisted. What was the cause of this powerful action? Was it not the tracks that guided the train? To a certain extent they did, but space itself had prescribed a track of its own. When the tracks curved sharply, the track prescribed for the train by space itself was obstructed, a conflict arose between two mighty powers, and in the heat of the combat heavy steel was bent and human lives were lost. One of the mighty powers in this conflict was the innocent looking "nothingness" we call empty space. It was the external, physically active space that here revealed its power; our mental space only served as a framework for the registration of the events and made possible the preservation of the pictures in our memory.

Physical space governs not only the motions of material bodies, but also the propagation of light. For the present we are not concerned with the velocity of bodies, but only with that quality of motion we call direction. By sighting along the tracks in the example just mentioned we could see whether the tracks were curved or straight—if they appeared straight the train would have a tendency to follow them. The light from a distant star is guided by space itself, in fact, we can, if we wish, define and determine straightness by reference to light beams in empty space.

Let us now go back to our experience with the railroad train and think it over more carefully, and ask in what particular way the train "wanted to go." If there were nothing directly beneath to support the train, it would obviously fall to the ground, a phenomenon which will be studied later. If the train were restrained in some way to move in a horizontal plane, but could freely move sideways, it would be interesting to find just how the invisible, mysterious space would guide it. To study this problem we shall replace the train by a heavy weight, suspended from a rigid support by a long wire. We move the weight to one side and let go of it, being careful not to give it any push sideways. The pendulum begins to swing back and forth and we mark the plane of swing by a straight line on the floor beneath. It is important that the ball of the pendulum should be so shaped that the air resistance is not too large and has no tendency to move the ball to one side. If the pendulum is large and the ball heavy and properly shaped, it can keep on moving for many hours, although naturally the amplitude of the swing gradually decreases.

After a while we notice that the plane of swing is slowly but steadily turning. As seen from above, the plane of swing turns in the same direction as the hands of a clock. We repeat the experiment and get the same result. We take the pendulum to other places on the earth and find that the rate at which the plane of swing turns depends upon the geographic latitude. Near the north pole of the earth the plane of swing turns at such a rate that it would come back in its original position in twenty-four hours. As we approach the equator the rate of turning is slower, and at the equator it does not turn at all. When we pass to the southern hemisphere the direction of the turning of the plane of swing is reversed.

What is the cause of this peculiar phenomenon? The air has nothing to do with it, because we can perform the experiment even better in a vacuum. No hand has touched the pendulum after it was started, it has obeyed regulations, not imposed by human hands or minds. The earth has certainly something to do with the downward pull that turns it back after it has passed the lowest point in its swing, but the earth could not turn the plane of swing. If it could do anything at all in this respect, we should rather expect it to keep the plane of swing fixed in relation to itself. We go outside and look around. There is the sun setting in the west, there is the full moon rising in the east, and there are already a few bright stars appearing in the sky, and we know that there are millions of them we do not see. They all move from the east to the west, that is, in the same direction in which the plane of swing turns both in the northern and the southern hemisphere. Could they in some mysterious way influence the motion of the pendulum? It seems incredible—these bodies are all so far, far away.

When the railroad train was derailed at the curve in the tracks we said that space itself was guiding it along a straight path. Space also guides the pendulum in its motion, and the turning of the plane of swing of "Foucault's Pendulum," as such a device is called, tells us that if the train could freely move in a horizontal surface, it would in general not move quite "straight" on the earth's surface. If the train moved from the north or south pole toward the equator it would not follow the great circles from pole to pole, but would tend to move westward on the globe, guided by space itself. The winds show clearly this guiding influence.

The complication arises from the fact that the earth itself is turning, relative to external space. Space is not directly perceptible to our senses, but tracks of moving bodies and light beams are. The earth rotates relative to light beams, and the stars are so far away that the direction of stellar light beams is not sensibly affected by their motions. Hence we can determine the rotation of the earth relative to space by determining its rotation relative to stellar light beams. If we place a pendulum at one of the poles of the earth, the plane of swing turns around in one day relative to the earth beneath, but it remains stationary if we refer its motion to the beams of light from the stars. The pendulum tends to move in the same way as light does, it is governed by the same agency. If we place the pendulum at the equator, there can be no turning of the plane of swing, since the axis of the earth's rotation is there horizontal.

We begin now vaguely to see that space has an objective reality, it has properties and there are definite rules for its activities. But we should not call it a "material" substance and compare it with material bodies, as was the custom not so long ago, when physicists regarded space as filled with a hypothetical substance called *ether*. We might say that space has a *structure*,[1] that this structure determines the direction of propagation of light and moving bodies, and that the earth rotates relative to this structure. We shall later become acquainted with other structures of similar type, although apparently much more complex.

[1] This term is defined on page 40.

CHAPTER 2

Time

L ET US now go back to our own individual consciousness and contemplate what goes on in
our minds. The term "goes on" implies in itself that
something is changing. Pictures follow one another,
one sound is replaced by another, day is followed by
night—and life by death. In our consciousness is a
sequence of sensations and feelings from birth to
death. By the aid of a mental faculty called *memory*, we are conscious of the existence of this sequence
up to a definite point called *now*. New sensations
are added to the storehouse of memories. The sequence grows, apparently "new" moments replace
the old—and the series of remembered moments,
terminating with the present moment "now," is
called the *sequence of time in consciousness*.

Conscious time has only one dimension, and the
two opposite directions can be distinguished from
one another. Two different sensations may sometimes occur so close together in time that we may be
in doubt which was felt first, but, if they are sufficiently separated in time, we are never in doubt which
one came "first." Sometimes our memory may fail

us, and we may not be sure which one of two events occurred first, but we feel sure that this is due to a mental defect, and that the sequence of events in itself was unique and impossible of change. If we have several sensations at the same time, they may merge into one, or one may suppress all the others— we cannot separate them by "going sideways" in time. An event is either before or after another or both occur apparently at the same time. The sequence of conscious moments or conceptual time has thus properties similar to those of a directed line, and it is often represented symbolically by an arrow.

Conscious time does not appear to be continuous. It is broken by periods of unconsciousness or dreamless sleep, and may even be interrupted by periods of amnesia when part of the remembered time is temporarily lost. These phenomena are connected with changes in the activities in our brain and consciousness.

If a man had no memory, he would probably never arrive at a conception of time. For him there would apparently be only one moment, "now." For a being whose memory has a limited range, there is similarly only one interval of time, which is covered by his own remembered "life." Further, if the world around us were not changing, if a man saw the same picture, heard the same sound and had exactly the same sensation and the same emotion all his life, he would have great difficulty in conceiving any sequence of time, since one part of the "arrow of time" could not be distinguished from another part. Hence man's notion of time is dependent upon the perfection of his memory and upon the degree of change in his sensations and emotions.

When several individuals compare their sense impressions by signals and descriptions, they realize that they often have the same sensations at the same time. One of them throws a stone, they all see the moving body and hear it hitting the ground. Phenomena observable by several individuals are said to occur in an *external world*, which also includes those phenomena in our own bodies, which are observed by sense organs and can, at least in principle, be verified by observations by several individuals. The observation of motion is one of our first experiences of a new element in the external world, besides that of space, which we have previously considered. This new element we call *external* or *physical time*.

Physical time can be measured by *clocks*. A clock consists of a system in which some parts are moving relatively to other parts and where the rate of relative motion can be determined. A falling stone can be used as a clock by setting up a graduated pole close to the path, the marks being read as the stone passes by. The planet Jupiter with its moving satellites is often used as a clock by mariners, who want to find their longitude at sea, and so is the moon as it slowly moves in relation to the fixed stars. The pulse beats can also be used as a clock. Galileo used them when he discovered the laws of motions of the swinging candelabra in the cathedral of Pisa in 1581. The most convenient clocks are those in which the motion is periodic, and where the state of motion repeats itself with high accuracy. In a mechanical clock we hence keep the general physical conditions constant; we keep the temperature, air pressure and gravity unchanging, the last by keeping the clock at a fixed place, instead of letting it fall and hit something.

To study the changing phenomena in the external world we may use many clocks, but, since we want our observations to be independent of the particular clock we are using we compare them from time to time with a *standard clock*. Then we can compare measurements made at different parts of the earth or at different times and arrive at rules which are independent of the peculiarities of the individual clock we are using. It would be conceivable to have a very good international clock kept somewhere, which regulated the speed of all our individual clocks by wireless impulses ("telechrone clocks"). But perfect mechanical clocks are difficult to make, and it has been found practical to use the earth itself as a standard clock, its rotation relative to the stellar frame furnishing an excellent unit of time which we call a "sidereal day." Clocks regulated by vibrating crystals of quartz have recently been developed, and they have such a high accuracy that even extremely small variations in the period of the earth's rotation can be detected.

Having learned what a clock is, we want to know what we can find out about the external world with our clocks. A clock alone gives little information, but when combined with scales or measuring rods to measure lengths, balances to measure forces and the weight of bodies, instruments to measure electric tension (voltage), flow of electricity (amperage), the pressure in fluids, and so on, we can find many interesting things of practical importance. By varying the conditions of our experiments we can also find out the general rules according to which "Nature" seems to work. What we study by this method, however, is only one aspect of the Universe, its *space and time aspect*. The reason why we use this expression is that in the final analysis our measurements can be expressed in terms of intervals of length and of time. The expressions are best given in mathematical form, since they contain certain factors, exponents, and ratios, which have a profound meaning.

With our clocks and yardsticks we can soon find that if we drop a body, it falls down, and for every second it covers more and more feet until it hits the ground. The number of feet (or other units of length) it travels per second we call its *velocity*, and when the velocity is increasing with time we say that the motion is accelerated. Rolling a body on a very smooth horizontal surface we find that its velocity decreases very slowly, and that it travels in a nearly straight line. That the line is straight means that we can find a place back of the moving body such that the body obscures the same portion of the background during its whole motion, although, of course, the body appears smaller and smaller. In other words the body moves nearly as "straight" as light does; its motion is also nearly uniform in time, although it decreases slowly. This decrease we say is due to friction at the surface and the resistance of the air, for, as we reduce these effects, the velocity tends to become more and more constant. The surface must be strictly horizontal, that is, every part of it must be parallel to the upper surface of the water in a vessel in the neighborhood. In this way we counteract the effects of the earth's gravity, which we regard as the "cause" of the accelerated downward motion of falling bodies.

We can also apply our measuring instruments to the sun, the moon, the planets and the stars. They are moving from the east to the west, a motion which we in the preceding chapter ascribed to the rotation of the earth relative to a structure in space. The celestial bodies are also moving relative to one another, and we find that such bodies, if sufficiently far apart, move for considerable intervals in straight lines and with uniform velocities relative to one another. The earth and the major planets move in nearly circular orbits around the sun according to definite rules, and the two components of a double star also move about one another according to similar rules. For celestial bodies the rules of motion are simpler than at the earth, since for the former we have no air resistance and collisions, practically speaking, never occur. For this reason the laws of motion of bodies in general are to a great extent based on astronomical observations.

The motions of bodies are influenced by other bodies in their neighborhood. We see it plainly in the planets whose motions are curved by the presence of the sun, and in the motions of bodies where we live, motions which are affected by the presence of the big globe beneath us all. Motions are also influenced by something we call magnetic and electric forces, which exert very large effects when bodies come close to one another. When we come to the study of the behavior of atoms we shall fully realize this fact.

We can also measure the speed of sound in air, water, or in solid bodies, and we find that it is different in different media. In this case no bodies are transmitted, what is transmitted is a *state of motion*. In a vacuum no sound at all can be transmitted. We can also measure the speed at which light travels in different media, like air, water, glass, and even in a vacuum. Light travels slower in the denser media, red light travels faster than blue light in the same medium, but in a vacuum light of all colors travels with the same speed. This is an extremely important fact. The velocity of sound in air, for instance, is obviously a property of the air, and we may similarly say that the velocity of light in empty space is a property of space itself. But since a velocity involves both space and time elements, *the constant of nature known as the velocity of light* IN VACUO *is a property of time as well as of space.* It furnishes a connecting link between space and time, indicating that these two fundamental entities in the external world are intimately bound together. We can now combine them into a wider concept, *space-time,* in which all physical phenomena appear to take place. This new concept has in Einstein's relativity theory acquired a great importance, transcending space and time, unifying the physical laws, and providing a powerful method of research both in *Macrocosmos* (the universe of stars) and in *Microcosmos* (the world within the atoms).

Let us now look back and see what we have found so far. We have found within our consciousness a frame of mental space and mental time,[1] in which

[1] According to Kant space and time are *a priori* "forms" for our perceptions. These "forms" correspond to what we here call mental space and mental time. After the advent of the theory of relativity scientists following Minkowski have learned to hypostatize space-time as an external counterpart to our mental space and time. Although physical space-time is a *mental* concept, it describes, albeit incompletely, a world *external* to the individual mind. The existence of physical space-time is de-

we place our visual pictures. Without sense organs
we should never have learned about space and without sense organs and memory we should never have
learned about time. Beyond ourselves there seems
to exist an external world with space and time properties, and the existence of this world can be ascertained
by comparing the simultaneous observations of many
individuals. The apparent motions are governed by
definite rules and the motions are modified by the
existence of neighboring bodies. Although there is
no visible link between space and time, they are
bound together by a certain constant relation, which
we call the velocity of light. A mysterious entity or
structure, space-time, governs the motions of particles
and stars, the propagation of light and radio waves,
and its subtle but powerful hand reaches into every
atom and every star in the universe; it reaches into
the tiniest cells of plants and animals, and even into
ourselves and our brains.

We have had a first glimpse of a reality beyond
men and the earth and the sun and the stars. Space
and time are unified; they appear no longer so intangible as they did when we started out on our

duced from collective knowledge derived empirically (*a pos-
teriori*), whereas mental space and mental time are derived from
individual introspection and are inherent and inherited properties of the human mind arising from certain specific elements
in the human germ plasm (Cf. p. 175 ff.). Since these elements
(ova genes) have their origin (Cf. p. 145 ff.) and association
(Cf. p. 181 ff.) in Cosmos, the "circle" is closed.

search.   Space-time is a "ghost" which seems to quiver with something, which we shall later see is akin to *Life* and *Consciousness*.

The distinguished mathematical physicist Hermann Weyl [1] once wrote about this cosmic structure of space and time: *"If it is not a god, it must certainly be a super-human giant."*

[1] Weyl, H., The Open World, p. 20.   The Terry Lectures, Yale University Press.   1932.

CHAPTER 3

Matter

THE PRINCIPAL phenomena we observe in the external world of space and time are connected with something we call *matter*. It is idle to inquire what matter intrinsically is; we can only describe the sensations we receive from it, the properties of different kinds of matter and the laws which seem to hold for this mysterious substance.

When early man began his investigations of the Universe, it was, as we said before, not space and time which interested him, but certain things which were useful to him as food, tools and weapons. He called them "substantial," since they did not vanish in his hands as the wind and the sunbeam he tried to grasp. A rock, a tree, an animal, and also his fellowmen appeared as something permanent in the world; although they could move or be moved from one place to another, their identity during motion seemed beyond doubt, even for fairly long time intervals. Water was not quite so substantial, it gave way for his pushing hands and he could not for long study a particular drop of water; it evaporated into nothingness or was lost in a larger mass of water.

When he observed that even a big tree might disappear in a fire, and a killed and eaten animal seemingly was gone forever, his idea of the permanence of matter received a serious setback. But matter could be subdivided into small parts, and if he carried the sub-division far enough he might conceive that the smallest parts retained, at least to some extent, their identity. This might be the case, even though matter were crushed, evaporated or burned, although, of course, the eye was no longer able to follow the smallest parts in their travels. To retain the cherished idea of the indestructibility of matter man thought that matter consisted of small parts which could not be further subdivided, and these were accordingly called *atoms*, which means nondivisible.

For a long time the theory of the existence of atoms was regarded as a good working hypothesis, one which could never be definitely proved, however, since atoms could never be observed as individuals. After the discovery of x-rays and of radio-activity, the actions of individual atoms could be actually observed. No one doubts nowadays their actual existence, or rather their existence is regarded as no less certain than that of the larger bodies.

There are different kinds of matter. We have rigid bodies, like stones, metals, and wood; semi-solid bodies, like jelly and flesh; fluid bodies, like water and mercury; and gaseous bodies, like air.

Certain bodies can become rigid, soft, fluid or gaseous by heating or cooling.

Material substances appear in their simplest form, when they are gaseous. The atoms can be single, as in the gas helium, they can occur in pairs as in the oxygen of the air, or in groups of relatively few atoms as in the gases from an oil-well. Groups of atoms are called *molecules*. In a gas the molecules move around at a very high rate of speed and collide frequently with one another. In air at ordinary temperature and pressure the molecules move with an average speed of about 1500 feet per second, but they can only move a few millionth parts of an inch before they collide with other molecules. No particular damage is done by these collisions. The molecules simply bounce off one another, or rebound against the walls of the vessel in which the gas is enclosed. At high temperature the motions become more violent, and, if the gas is compressed before it is heated, the number of molecules which hit the walls is correspondingly increased. Our automobiles are driven by the impact of gas molecules in the engine's cylinders, in which compressed air is heated by internal combustion.

In liquids the molecules do not rebound when they collide, but remain in some kind of association for a longer or shorter time interval. The velocities of the molecules are very much smaller than in gases. The collisions are no longer like that of elastic balls, and the reduced speed gives the inter-molecular forces time to come into play. If these forces are very weak, as in oxygen and even more in helium, they can only become active when the velocities are extremely small. Since the temperature is a measure of the speed of the molecules, we can understand why these and other so-called "permanent" gases require a very low temperature to become liquids.

When we cool water the molecular velocities become smaller, and the molecules begin to form aggregations of large numbers of molecules. Needles or flakes of ice begin to form and rise to the surface, they join together into a thin sheet which gradually thickens and forms solid ice. In molten metals the aggregations sink to the bottom, the hotter molten metal stays on top, and by further cooling the whole mass solidifies.

Most inorganic substances in the solid state consist of *crystals*, which are agglomerations of atoms in definite patterns. If we study ice or snow-flakes under a microscope, we see the most beautiful starlike bodies, made up of nothing but pure water in the solid state. Minerals consist of small crystals mixed together. Occasionally the dimensions of the crystals are surprisingly large.

If in the study of crystals we use x-rays instead of ordinary light, we can readily discover how the atoms are arranged. Taking a crystal of sodium chloride, which is ordinary table salt, we find the sodium and the chlorine atoms arranged in a simple cubic pattern, with a definite separation between the constituent atoms. In other crystals the pattern may be more complicated, but the same general structure exists everywhere, although crystals of the same chemical substance may differ in the same way as an object and its image in a mirror.

Different chemical substances occur in nature and we can change one substance into another by simple means. We can dissolve a metal in an acid and we can burn wood, oil, and many gases. A closer study of the chemical changes we can bring about in the substances on the earth has shown that there are a number of *chemical elements* which cannot be disrupted by ordinary means, and that all substances living and dead, gaseous, liquid and solid, are built up of these elements in different structural configurations and proportions.

When we let an electric current run through a closed tube of glass in which the air pressure is being reduced, several strange phenomena occur. The air in the tube begins to glow, dark and light spaces begin to show, and the general appearance changes greatly with the air pressure. At greatly reduced pressure a beam of faint light seems to extend from one of the electric terminals (the cathode), and where it strikes the glass we observe a greenish color. The beam can be deflected by a magnet and can thus not be "light" of any ordinary kind. J. J. Thomson made an exhaustive study of this phenomenon and found that the beam consisted of tiny particles which had a "negative" electric charge, and they are now called *electrons*. Their collision with the glass produces *x-rays* which, while invisible to the eye, cause a temporary luminosity (*fluorescence*) in a number of substances, and may also act on photographic plates (x-ray photographs).

We have said that the atoms and the molecules are extremely small, but the electrons are at least a thousand times smaller than the smallest atoms. They are always alike, can move with tremendous velocities and occur in all kinds of matter. They move quite freely in metals and their motion produces the electric current that flows in the wires running to our electric light bulbs, the electrons being continuously "pumped" into the wires by electric generators or batteries. When we stroke a cat's fur we remove electrons from the fur, and the resulting sparks are connected with certain activities in the electrified molecules of the air.

Electrons are a constituent of all kinds of matter. Atoms are "built" of electrons and *atomic nuclei*. The latter are much heavier than electrons and carry a "positive" electric charge. The terms positive and negative electricity were introduced by Franklin because he thought that the two known kinds of electricity were due to an excess and a deficiency, respectively, of a hypothetical electric fluid. We all know that when we rub glass with silk, the glass acquires what we call a positive electric charge, and when we rub a rod of sealing wax with cloth, the former acquires a negative charge. Nowadays we know more about the process and we realize that when glass is rubbed with silk electrons are removed from the surface of the glass and are caught on the silk, and if a rod of sealing wax is rubbed with a woolen cloth electrons are transferred from the cloth to the rod. Since positive and negative electricity neutralize one another, the loss in the normally neutral glass gives it a positive electricity. If a metal is brought in contact with the positively charged glass, the glass recaptures the lost electrons, and the metal becomes positively charged. Charged bodies show mutual attractions, if they have opposite charges, and repulsion, if they have charges of the same kind.

The electrons we study in the vacuum tube appeared as small particles having a definite, negative electric charge. When the electrons occur in atoms they probably "look" quite different. Of course we do not "see" them in any event, it is only their effect on gross matter which we can study. But modern physics has found out many things about atoms, especially by shooting electrons and atoms with high speed into matter of different kinds. We cannot here describe the methods, we shall simply state the results and describe the inner structure of some of the atoms.

The simplest atom is that of hydrogen. Ordinary hydrogen gas consists of molecules each of which is built up of two atoms. Each atom has a "heart" or "nucleus" of positive electricity surrounded by an atmosphere [1] of negative or electronic electricity. Most of the mass is concentrated in the central nucleus, the atmosphere contributing only about one two-thousandth part of the whole. The atmosphere must not be thought of as a spherical envelope, like that of the earth's atmosphere, its structure is very complicated and depends upon or rather determines the "state" of the atom. For some unknown reason the negative electricity does not combine with the positive electricity in the center—mysterious forces hold the nucleus together and separate the positive and negative electricity. When light of a certain *frequency* (color) strikes the atom, the atmosphere becomes disturbed and seems in a certain sense to "expand." After the light-impulse has ceased, the atmosphere falls back to its original state, and the atom emits *radiation* (light) of a certain frequency. If the hydrogen atom is violently struck by another atom, it may apparently lose its whole "negative" atmosphere, which then goes off as a lump of nega-

[1] This term as here used represents the Schrödinger waves and the extra-nuclear electrons in the usual model.

tive electricity—an electron. A hydrogen atom which has lost its electron is said to be an *ion* or be *ionized*, it carries a positive charge and is simply a hydrogen nucleus, or a *proton*. When it again catches an electron from the outside, the electron is incorporated in the electric atmosphere of the nucleus. This transformation does not take place in one "jump," the electron seems to "fall down" a number of steps, each one being associated with the emission of light of different, but definite frequencies and *wave lengths*. An atom in which the atmosphere has settled down into its lowest, most stable state, is said to be in the "ground state," an atom in which the atmosphere is disturbed is said to be *excited*. The sparks we see in electric discharges and the glow in vacuum tubes are due to ionized or excited atoms reorganizing their atmospheres and at the same time throwing out the excess energy to surrounding space in the form of visible or invisible light of different frequencies.

When the internal constitution of atoms was investigated by Rutherford, it was thought that the laws of motion of the electrons in the atoms were the same as those governing matter in bulk. The observable radii of electrons and of atomic nuclei were found to be about a hundred thousand times smaller than the atoms themselves. In Bohr's original model of a hydrogen atom the electron was supposed to go round a nucleus as a planet goes round the sun, the mutual attraction between the two being balanced by centrifugal forces due to their relative motion. Although this model explained practically every observed fact about hydrogen, later investigations showed that we are not permitted to apply the ordinary conceptions of matter in motion to the tiny world within the atom. A new mechanics, the so-called *wave-mechanics*, had to be introduced, of which we shall speak more in the next chapter.

The different chemical elements of which the material world is built have atomic nuclei with different charges and different masses. The elements can be arranged in a series in which the electric charge of the nucleus is an integral multiple of that of the hydrogen nucleus, the proton. The charges are always positive, never has an atomic nucleus been found which has a negative charge. The series starts with hydrogen, (atomic number equal to "one") which has a single charge; next comes helium, (atomic number two) which has a charge of two units, lithium with a charge of three, beryllium four, boron five, carbon six, nitrogen seven, oxygen eight, aluminum thirteen, iron twenty-six, zinc thirty, gold seventy-nine, up to uranium which has a charge exactly ninety-two times that of the hydrogen nucleus. When this law was first discovered, it was for the first time possible to "call the roll" of the chemical elements found by men on earth. Nearly all the ninety-two elements were found to be present, a few missing elements were discovered later, and only two are still to be found.

The masses of the atomic nuclei vary also in a way similar to that of the electric charges. The masses are also integral multiples of a common unit, and in many cases a given chemical element can have masses of different sizes. For instance, hydrogen with a weight twice that of ordinary hydrogen exists in nature, and bromine with atomic weights 79 and 81 occur in nearly equal abundance.

At a low temperature, as at the surface of the earth, the atomic nuclei are surrounded by negative electrons, and the number of electrons is just equal to the atomic number. An atom, a molecule, or matter in bulk, has hence in general no electric charge, it is electrically *neutral*. Matter can be electrified by different methods. We can rub off some electrons from the surface and we have "frictional electricity," we can put plates of zinc and copper in a dilute acid, and different charges will accumulate on the metallic plates ("galvanic electricity"), we can move a piece of metal rapidly in a magnetic field, and the free electrons in the metal will move in certain directions ("induced electricity" in generators), we can illuminate certain metals, and electrons will be given off ("photo electricity"), we can evaporate electrons in metals by applying heat ("thermal electricity"), and the sun heats the oceans and the water vapors carry electric charges to the clouds ("atmospheric electricity"). These different methods all depend upon either a transfer of electrons from atoms or on the forced motion of a group of free electrons in electric or magnetic fields.

It is of great importance for us to know that the light given out by an atom is of definite frequencies (color) dependent upon the emitted energy, and the latter is also of definite amounts, dependent upon the atomic structure and the state of the electric atmosphere. The energy emitted divided by the frequency of the radiation is always equal to a certain unit of "action," which we call the *quantum of action*. The discovery of this universal constant is one of the greatest achievements of modern science. It has profoundly modified our concept of atoms and of radiation and opened up a new world for our studies.

The atmosphere of negative electricity around the atomic nuclei is a complicated structure. The outer parts determine alone the chemical properties of the atom. Certain structures, like those of the inert gases, are so symmetrical in all directions, that one must come extremely close to them before the electrical forces become manifest. Others have one or two electrons beyond the main atmosphere. Only through extremely violent encounters or through radiation by high frequency (x-rays) can we upset the equilibrium of the lower parts of the atmosphere and learn its secrets. The nucleus itself, however, is in general not reached by such methods, and its small dimensions relative to the atom itself was for a long time unknown. With the discovery of *radio-active elements* our knowledge increased tremendously. These elements have nuclei which spontaneously disintegrate, with ejection of electrons, *α-particles* (which are nuclei of helium), and *gamma rays* (which are x-rays of very high frequency). Certain radio-active elements only last a fraction of a second, others like radium last for a few thousand years. By shooting particles of extremely high speed at ordinary atoms we can produce changes in the structure of the atomic nuclei and thus change one chemical element into another. During this transformation bodies of unexpected properties are sometimes ejected. *Neutrons,* having no charge at all and with the same mass as protons, are ejected by beryllium. Positive electrons, also called *positrons,* are ejected at some reactions.

It would carry us too far to describe all the atomic properties of matter; in the present study we want simply to emphasize that matter has an extremely complicated structure, and that it appears to be "built up" of very small elements, having definite masses and definite electric charges, positive and negative. A better understanding of matter will be reached in the next chapter, where we study more closely the fields in which atoms move and the entities which marshal the elementary parts in the material world in organized units and patterns.

CHAPTER 4

Gravitational and Electrical Fields

O NE OF the earliest discoveries of man was that bodies have weight, and that if a body were lifted from the ground it always fell down again. The weight was measured by the muscular effort needed to lift the body from the ground, and gravity was hence early regarded as similar to the pull on a body exerted by man or beast with rods or ropes. The absence of any visible connection between the earth, which is seemingly responsible for the pull, and the body itself has never ceased to puzzle mankind. Many theories have been proposed to explain the mystery or to express the interaction in mechanical terms, but we have gradually begun to realize that we are dealing with properties of matter and space, so fundamental that mechanical pictures or models are inadequate, erroneous, or misleading. Modern physics does not try to "explain" gravity, it expresses the laws according to which it acts and regards its existence as one of the most fundamental properties of matter in its relation to the space and time of the universe.

Scientists ever since Galileo's and Newton's fundamental discoveries and theories have expended much time and ingenuity in finding the quantitative laws which govern the motion of bodies at the earth's surface and in the universe around us. The nature of motion in general is much more complex than we usually realize, for it involves the constancy of the length of the rods or tapes by which we measure distances, the constancy of the rate of the clock by which we measure time intervals, the progagation of light from the moving object to our eyes, the transformation of a physical or chemical process on the retina of our eyes to a mental sensation in our consciousness, and our inborn idiosyncrasies in describing and interpreting our sensations in familiar terms. It is generally recognized that in order to define motion quantitatively we must everywhere have a so-called "metrical field," which determines at every point the spacing of atoms in our measuring rods, the rate of our clocks, the propagation of light, and also the motions of the bodies themselves. Since motions are expressible in terms of space and time intervals, we often use the term "space-time" instead of a metrical field, because, whatever terms we use, it is only the space-time properties of the field that can be studied by our explorations with light rays and with moving test particles. We are not here concerned with the quantitative laws of gravity, except that the existence of definite, rational rules for motion is in itself an important datum in our experience. We are more concerned with an analysis and an interpretation of matter and motion which may help us in our study of the nature of the Universe.

In the first chapter we said that there was some connection between the tendency of the railroad train to move in a straight line and space itself. When we studied Foucault's pendulum we saw dimly that there was some connection between the turning of the plane of swing and the stars far out in space. That part of the universe which we call material is mostly concentrated in stars of which our sun is one, and what we call "empty space" is a field with definite properties, which regulates the motions of bodies and the propagation of light. We cannot say that matter is the "cause" of the metrical properties of space-time; matter, as manifested by its space and time properties, is one of the many "aspects" of the universe.

In the case of the railroad train we must remember that the earth and the rails consist of atoms, each surrounded by electrical fields of which we shall speak presently. These atomic fields have the property of mutual repulsion at small distances, and this repulsion prevents the atoms from penetrating each other and the whole earth from collapsing into a

tiny ball of extremely high density.[1] The atoms—
or rather the electric atmosphere of the atoms—in
the earth and in the rails prevent the train from falling down, and it is guided by the field in the simplest
possible kind of motion, which is "straight" and "uniform." In this picture we have assumed that the
engineer gives the engine just enough steam to com-
pensate for the air resistance and the friction of the
wheels against the rails. If he wants the train to
deviate to the right or left, the only way to do it is
to let the electric atmospheres of atoms press against
the train, and that is exactly what happens when the
rails are curved and their atoms press against the
flanges of the wheels. When we stand on the ground
and feel the weight of our body pressing against the
ground, it is not the attraction of the earth we notice
the most, but rather the hammering of the atoms in
the ground or in the bottoms of our shoes against the
soles of our feet.

If a man is freely falling, he feels no effect of
gravity, although he may feel the air rushing past
him. In a formal sense gravity has disappeared so
far as he is concerned. An outside observer, however, who can simultaneously study and contemplate
the motions of the falling man in conjunction with
that of the earth and other bodies, would not admit

---

[1] Such "collapsed" bodies occur in the universe as extremely
dense stars.

that gravity has in any way disappeared—it has in a sense changed from a potentiality to an actuality. The study of the appearance of a gravitational field for observers moving in different ways helped Einstein to formulate the quantitative expressions governing the properties of space-time.

The following question has sometimes been raised. If there were no other stars than the sun in the whole universe, would there be a perceptible change in the physical world? Would the physical constants be the same, would the inertial motion of the railroad train or of Foucault's pendulum be the same as before, and so on? The problem can be reversed and the following question be asked. Can we from observations in a physical laboratory, without looking out through a telescope at distant suns and nebulae, tell if there are other suns far out in space and how many there are?

First it should be noted that the physical constants of nature which we determine in the laboratory are given in terms of arbitrary units of mass, length and time. The units are usually grams, centimeters, and seconds, respectively. If we use other units we find other values for these same constants. Physical theories are beginning to become more and more comprehensive, and we find relations between the constants of nature which should hold if our theories were correct. By combining the different values for the observed constants we arrive at pure numbers, which obviously are independent of the units we use in our measurements. One of these numbers is the ratio of the mass of a proton to that of an electron. Its value is about 1840. Another is the velocity of light [1] expressed in atomic units, its value is 137. A third number is the ratio of the electric force between an electron and a proton to the gravitational force between them. This number is 23.10^{38}, that is, 23 followed by 38 ciphers.

Sir Arthur Eddington has made a profound study of this problem and has arrived at the conclusion that this last number is dependent on the total number of atoms in the whole universe. This number is equivalent to 10^{79} hydrogen atoms! This is an extremely large number and the study of the extragalactic nebulae and their motions offers some support for this estimate.

If Eddington's theory is correct,[2] it would mean

[1] This number is usually referred to as the fine-structure constant $(hc/2\pi e^2)$. It can also be regarded as the ratio of the unit of action manifested in radiation phenomena $(h/2\pi)$ and the unit of action in the orbit of an electron around a proton (e^2/c).

[2] Other explanations of the large number here referred to have been given. Dirac has recently called attention to the fact that the number $23 \cdot 10^{38}$ is equal to the time $(2.10^9$ years) it has taken the extra-galactic nebulae to reach their present distances (assuming the red shift in their spectra to indicate actual recession), if this time is expressed in atomic units (e^2/mc^3). If his explanation is correct the constants of nature are slowly but steadily changing, a possibility previously emphasized and studied by Zwicky. The stability of atoms may in this case be steadily

that, if there were no stars and nebulae beyond the solar system, electrical forces would be much smaller, when compared with the gravitational attractions, than we find them. Perhaps atomic nuclei which are now stable would then be unstable on account of the weakening of the effect of electric fields relative to that of gravitational fields. (Cf. p. 184)

I have cited this work of Eddington simply to show that scientists are beginning to realize the interdependence of matter, space, and time, and the connection between the atomic scale and the cosmic scale. Microcosmos and macrocosmos appear as different aspects of a common entity—a conception which we shall find extremely useful in our later studies of the nature and origin of life and of the relationship between mind and matter.

The gravitational attraction between bodies of the size we ordinarily handle is extremely small, although it is possible to measure with fair accuracy the attraction of two bodies each weighing about a pound. Gravity appears to us so overwhelming because we are living on a very massive globe of matter, the earth, and each of the atoms in this globe makes its contribution to the field. But attractions can be caused by other means than by gravity, it can be produced by electric and magnetic fields, and such fields

increasing, ever since the time of their first formation. In any event, it is practically a necessity to regard the physical properties of Cosmos as being intimately related to those of the atoms.

may also produce repulsion instead of attraction. The electric attraction or repulsion between two pound-weights can be very much greater than their gravitational attraction. It depends not upon their mass or weight, but upon their electric charge. We have previously spoken of the electric nature of the elements of which atoms are built, and hence, if the positive and negative elements are of equal number, a body is electrically neutral, so far as external effects are concerned. If there is an excess of positive or negative elements, the body is said to have a positive or a negative electric charge, respectively.

The discovery by Oersted that an electric current acts on a compass needle was followed by Ampère's important discoveries of the relationship between electricity and magnetism. When the phenomena of electricity and magnetism were further investigated by Faraday, he realized that the apparent "forces" must in some way be inherent in the *space* around the attracting or repelling bodies. This view was formally expressed in Maxwell's equations which describe the structure in space and time of the field around the bodies involved, a structure which can be pictured as consisting of a system of lines of force. For a time it was thought that ultimately this structure would be attributed to some kind of "ether" in which the bodies were imbedded, but gradually it became evident that the description itself of the space-time properties of the field was the only thing with which physics was concerned, and that the ultimate nature of electricity and magnetism was not at all involved in this description.

Modern developments in physics have completely vindicated this conception. Therefore when we describe electricity and gravity, radiation and motion, dead and living matter, it is *space-time structures*[1]

[1] The word *structure* is used extensively in this book but is applied only to spatial and spatio-temporal relations. In a two-dimensional space the structure can be described by intersecting or non-intersecting lines which represent constant values of certain properties (e.g. density). If the lines intersect, the structure can form a network (reticular structures). In a three-dimensional space the structure can be represented by lines and by surfaces, and fibrillar and cellular structures and many singularities can make their appearance. Space-time is a four-dimensional continuum in which the time axis is the fourth dimension. Its structure can be represented by lines, surfaces and hypersurfaces, and it can have many types of singularities. Space-time structures can also be visualized as a continuous record of space patterns. A good illustration is a moving picture film of the changing structure of a living cell. In this case the structure represents the changing optical properties of the cell which are closely related to its changing electrical structure. The appearance and characteristics of structures depend upon the degree of resolving power, and thus arises the difference between the everyday and the scientific world as exemplified by the crude pictures of our direct vision, the more detailed pictures seen in a microscope, and the even more refined mental pictures derived from indirect observations and by calculations. With high resolving power in space and time, space-time structures can usually be described as "wave systems" or "frequency patterns." Simple structures like atoms and molecules can be characterized by a set of *numbers* which must be regarded as intrinsic properties of the external world. Since mathematics is the science of numbers and structures, its results and symbolic language are used in physics.

The physical aspect of both causal and teleological phenomena and nothing else that we describe. What electricity and radiation, atoms and stars, plants and animals represent in the external world and what characteristics they may possess apart from their physical, that is, structural, properties are problems which belong to some other field than that of physics, chemistry, astronomy, or biology. As yet this field is largely unexplored, but an access to the same can be gained by a thorough investigation of the intrinsic nature and the origin of life and of mind. We must study matter *from within* and not solely from without. We must study the *substance* and not only the shadows.

Before attempting such a study we must investigate more closely the nature of motion and of material structures. I throw a stone into the air. At first its motion is determined by the motion of my arm and my hand. When it leaves my hand, its motion is determined by its inertia, the earth's gravitational field, and the resistance of the air. According to the relativity theory inertia and gravity are of similar nature, their combined effect on the motion is determined by the "potentials of the metrical field" in which the body is moving. With the discovery of the *quantum of action* by Planck, the confirmation of De Broglie's theory of the *wave properties of*

can be described by space-time structures since they do not distinguish between cause and effect but simply describe the sequence of events which we have observed in the past and which we expect to occur in the future.

material particles by Davisson and Germer and G. P. Thomson, and the enunciation and clarification of the *Principle of Indeterminacy* by Heisenberg and Bohr, it has become possible to obtain a picture of how the field really acts. It has been shown by Schrödinger that particles of matter are *guided* in their motion in the same way as light is guided. The latter can be described as a wave motion of some sort, and it has been found that particles also are guided by "waves" of certain types.

A simple case of motion is that of an electron in an electric field. Experiments show that an electron is guided in its motion by something which we, with pictorial conceptions founded on the observed motions of rigid and fluid bodies, may compare with waves or wave groups. They are called *wave packets* or *pilot waves* and determine the uncertainties in position and motion (or rather momentum) of the moving electron. The product of these uncertainties can never be smaller than the quantum of action. The pilot waves can thus only determine the position of an electron at a future time with a certain degree of probability. We may say that the electron is always within the pilot wave, but where it is and how it is moving within the wave is not determined by any physical laws at all.[1] The electron represents the

[1] Since our measuring devices are subject to the same unpredictable behavior as particles in general the indeterminacy is often regarded as due to the intrusion of an observer with his measuring tools, and the uncertainty as being brought about by

"observable" part of the combination, the pilot wave is our mental picture of the "hand" that guides it in space and time. The electron has a certain degree of "freedom," and many physicists believe that if there is anything at all that determines the position and motion of the electrons within the limits set by the quantum of action, this something may well be entirely outside the domain of physics. All physical laws are now regarded as being of a statistical type, like the mortality tables of a life insurance company. Although they appear to be extremely accurate when we are dealing with a great number of units, their real nature becomes evident when we study the effects of individual electrons and atoms.

The Principle of Indeterminacy can be applied to all physical phenomena. In optics it can be used to explain the diffraction and interference of light. It explains the spreading out of electron beams in definite patterns when reflected by metallic crystals, and many other similar phenomena.

Inside the atoms we can not study the motions of the individual particles. What we study is the properties of atoms averaged over a certain time interval, and the atoms hence appear as structures in space alone. If the internal motions are such that the state

the act of observation. The concept of pilot waves as guiding the electrons in space-time seems to the writer to be not only the best pictorial representation but also a means of emphasizing a dual nature of the phenomena of motion and of structure, which is of extreme importance in the present study.

of motion does not change with time, the atoms appear as stable structures; if the average state of motion changes with time, the atom appears to be unstable. Hence certain structures appear more stable than others; an excited atom, for instance, may on its own account settle down to a more stable state, and during this process it emits certain amounts of energy in the form of radiation. An ionized atom can capture an electron and, in going through all the intermediary steps of reorganization until it reaches its most stable state, it emits a great number of *definite* energy amounts. Each of these represents a line in the spectrum of the atom, and it is by a study of these lines that we have obtained most of our information about atomic structures.

The atomic nuclei also have structures, although of a more compact form. Most atomic nuclei are very stable, but, as we have said before, the atomic nuclei of the radioactive elements are unstable. Some may last for hundreds of thousands of years, whereas others may only last a very small fraction of a second.

Let us picture the nucleus of an atom of radium. Within its structure is an α-particle (helium atom) with high energy. The pilot waves of the α-particle extend beyond the potential barriers of the nucleus. There is hence a definite probability that the α-particle will find itself outside the boundaries of the nucleus.

It may take a minute or a few thousand years before this occurs, but when it does, the α-particle leaves the radium atom and guided by pilot waves it moves out into space. The wave system in the radium atom is now very unstable, it tries to reorganize itself by throwing out more α-particles, electrons, and excess energy in the form of gamma rays. After several unsuccessful attempts it finally reaches a stable state —as an atom of lead.

What we have said here points to the existence of a *dualism* in the physical world. The dual aspect is often referred to as the "particle aspect" and the "wave aspect." For reasons which will later become evident we shall regard the two aspects as belonging to two different "worlds," which we designate by the terms *material* and *immaterial*. An electron will be regarded as belonging to the material world; electrical fields, radio waves and pilot waves will be regarded as belonging to the immaterial world. A neutron is material, its gravitational field is immaterial. An atom consists of *particles*, neutrons, positrons, electrons (perhaps also photons and neutrinos), which are cemented together into a unit by an *immaterial wave-structure* with certain space and time properties. It is this structure which "organizes" and "inflates" atoms, molecules, crystals, and solid bodies in general. In modern physics it is often described as a complex system of "energy levels" or "quantum cells." The mysterious *forces* of classical physics can be regarded as manifestations of such immaterial structures.

A positron is probably a structure which in some way is the "reversal" of an electron. The fact that all atomic nuclei have a positive electric charge and appear to have protons and neutrons as their sole constituents, indicates that there exists a great "structural affinity" between neutrons and positrons or their pilot waves.[1] The fields of electrons and positrons are electric and complementary. The fields of neutrons are gravitational and accumulative, since no reversals of neutrons seem to exist in our universe.

Gravitational and electric fields are often regarded as being "caused" by the elementary particles of matter. But our ordinary notion of cause and effect is not applicable to this case, because we can not destroy or create matter and energy and study the consequences. Although there are reasons to believe that the particles in some way or other are the cause of the wave systems, the connection between the guiding field and the guiding waves on the one hand and the particles guided by them on the other hand is still

[1] It has been suggested that neutrons may be combinations of protons and electrons. If we make such an assumption we are left with no explanation for the existence of positively charged atomic nuclei and the non-existence of negatively charged nuclei. Recent experiments have shown that neutrons are probably more fundamental constituents of matter than protons.

very obscure. Many physicists regard them as different "aspects" of an unknown reality of which the human mind has only a very imperfect comprehension.

Particles seem to be energy in a very concentrated form, and the guiding waves determine where we may expect to find these bundles of energy. A particle does not "know" at all where to stay or where to go; it is the guiding field and the guiding waves which determine its position and motion, although only within certain limits fixed by the size of the quantum of action. If it is necessary to postulate guiding fields and guiding waves to explain the structures and motions in the inorganic world, it is obvious that it is even more necessary to do this for the much more complicated structures and changes in the living world, as we shall see later.

It has been found that the energy in light beams also seems to be concentrated in bundles called *photons*, which have properties similar to those of particles.[1] These photons are also guided by waves in their motions in space and time, in fact the field and the waves guiding the propagation of light were recognized long before those guiding the particles of matter. To ask *what* this mysterious field and these mysterious waves are is useless, our sense organs and

[1] Although a photon carries energy and momentum it should, nevertheless, be regarded as immaterial because its "rest mass" is zero. The absence of any inherent, residual mass is the cause of the fixed velocity of "free" or "unattached" photons.

our inherited mental faculties are of such a nature that the only description we can make of the field and the waves is in terms of space and time, that is, as "structures in space-time." As pointed out before physical science does not pretend to reach beyond such a description.

Both matter and light appear to us as consisting of "particles" and "waves." The latter as their name implies have space and time properties, usually expressed in terms of wave lengths, frequencies and velocities. The propagation of the particles is governed by the field acting on the wave systems, but the particles themselves seem to be responsible for the essential space-time properties of the system. Particles at rest have energies, masses, angular momenta, and in some cases at least electric charges, of certain definite amounts, a fact which indicates that they have properties which can not be expressed in terms of our concept of continuous space and time. Furthermore, a theory of matter which does not take into consideration the phenomena of life and gives no expression for the peculiarities of the human mind can not be regarded as satisfactory. If we want to comprehend the nature of and the relationship between matter, life and mind, a fundamental change in our ideas is necessary. The following picture [1] gives us an im-

[1] This picture was developed after the first edition (in Swedish) appeared in 1938. It was derived by inductive reasoning from a number of facts most of which are described in the following chapters, but it is here used as a starting point in a more

portant lead which we shall follow in our further studies of the nature, development and origin of life and of mind.

There is another world than that of space and time. The two worlds are not completely separated; they interact at certain points or *sources* around which we observe wave systems of different types. Some of these points we identify with "material" particles, and through some of them an entity we call "electricity," the ultimate nature of which we know nothing, enters the domain of space and time. Other contact points are "immaterial"; they are the sources for "living" wave systems of different degrees of complexity. Some contact points are associated with certain nerve centers in our brain—and they are the roots of our consciousness and the sources of all our knowledge.

All our knowledge of matter is directly or indirectly inferred from mental sensations. The pictures in our consciousness which we see with our eyes are *mental* pictures, the rules we derive from our observations and express in our equations are *mental* rules, and the models in space and time which we construct to describe and to explain physical phenomena are *mental* models. Our *mental* framework

---

deductive theory. I realized later that the picture has a certain resemblance to Leibnitz' monadological theories. The theory of monads probably originated with Pythagoras, was reintroduced in philosophy by Giordano Bruno and has often been revived in philosophical systems, although not on a strictly scientific basis.

of space and time has made possible our cognition of a physical world. The mental model of atoms and solid bodies which most physicists have today looks like a system of compartments in which the elementary particles of matter apparently can move in any way they please, without gain or loss of energy, a "motion" which by its very nature is inaccessible to observation and for this reason is often regarded as an unnecessary or perhaps illegitimate mental construction. It has been found that there can never be more than one of these particles in the same structural compartment (Pauli's Exclusion Principle). The structure of atoms is in general so complicated that it can not be pictured in the three-dimensional space [1] for the perception of which we seem to have inherited a special facility.

When the particles in our mental atomic models move to new levels and when the structure is changing, we expect something to happen—and this is our mental picture of the events in the external world when light is emitted from a luminous body. The pictures are all mental; we feel certain that there exists something external to our mind, but we should be careful not to identify the mental pictures with

---

[1] This fact has been used as an argument against the *objective* reality of the wave systems. It seems, however, that the complication mentioned is due to the fact that in our observations we can not distinguish one electron from another and hence must describe them as groups defined by their statistical properties.

the external world itself. We have learned to distinguish between a man and his photograph, but only few of us have learned to distinguish between the external world and the shadows from this world in our consciousness.

CHAPTER 5

Living Matter and Organisms

W E HAVE said that there are many different kinds of matter and at least ninety-two different kinds of atoms. Atoms combine to form molecules and chemical substances, some stable, others transitory, depending upon the strength of the electric bonds. The structure of a few of the largest molecules can be seen in ultraviolet light, but most molecules require the finer light of the x-rays to be recognized as individuals. Matter in different form is all around us, in the earth, the moon and the planets, in the sun and the stars of the great star system we call The Milky Way, and in the faraway galaxies, each consisting of millions of suns.

There is one particular place in this whole universe, where we know that there exists a very remarkable kind of substance, which we call *Living Matter*. This place is the surface of the tiny planet on which we live. Many astronomers think that it may well be the only place where this kind of matter exists, or at least that there are extremely few places in the universe where we may hope to find this extraordinary type of matter. The plants, the animals, and you and I are built of it. It is even in some way or other associated with our consciousness.

What then are the reasons for the assumption that living matter or, as we usually call it, organic life, is so exclusive in regard to its habitat? We have not penetrated into the deep interior of the earth or visited the planets, the sun or the stars. In fact, we have not even been outside the earth's atmosphere. The reason is that organic life as we know it requires for its development very special conditions, particularly with regard to temperature. Biologists believe that certain chemical elements, in particular carbon, hydrogen, oxygen and nitrogen, are necessary constituents in living matter. Living matter must be in a *liquid* form, or at least a great portion of a living organism must be liquid. The liquid around which the organisms on the earth are built is water and, since water in fluid form can only exist at a relatively small temperature range, the importance of the proper temperature becomes apparent. Low organisms can remain alive, although in a dormant stage, at extremely low temperatures if their water content is sufficiently small; they can probably remain alive even at the low temperature of inter-stellar space, but for their *development* it is necessary that they contain matter in liquid form.

The overwhelming part of the matter in the universe is in the form of stars, which have a very high temperature, all the matter in them being in a gaseous state.   Organic life, as we know it, cannot exist there, although other types of "life" may well exist there as everywhere else, as we shall explain later.   It is only on the surface of planets that we can have the proper temperature conditions and that liquids like water can exist.   The planet should not be too small, for then the water would soon evaporate and disappear, even if we in some mysterious way could get the water there.   Thus the moon and the asteroids are not supposed to be suitable abodes for organic life.   The planet must be near a sun in order to receive a sufficient amount of heat to prevent the water from being permanently frozen.   The larger planets in the solar system contain large amounts of ammonia and methane, and Venus contains an abundance of carbon dioxide.   They all contain practically no free oxygen in their atmosphere, and it may well be questioned whether there are types of organic life that can develop under such conditions.   Further, according to the prevalent ideas about the formation of our solar system the existence of planets near the stars is an extremely rare phenomenon, and exceedingly few planetary systems are supposed to exist in the universe.[1]   It is now clear why the statement is often

[1] There is some doubt about the validity of this theory, however.   The amount of angular momentum per unit mass in the

FIG. I.

Cell Division.

(From *E. B. Wilson*, THE CELL. 1925.
By permission of The Macmillan Co.)

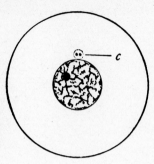

A. Resting cell showing the network in the nucleus, c is the centrosome with two components.

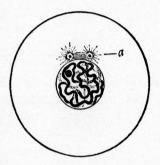

B. The network has become thicker and forms a continuous thread. The centrosomes have separated and the rays begin to develop.

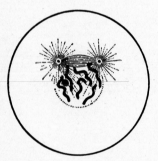

C. The chromosomes are now visible in the nucleus. The centrosomes are farther apart and the rays more extended.

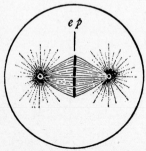

D. The chromosomes are lined up in the plane midway between the centrosomes, the rays of which are now fully extended and begin to contract.

E. The chromosomes can now be seen as doublets.

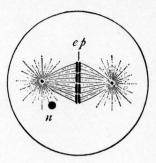

F. The components of the chromosomes are moving towards the respective centrosomes which now show double centers.

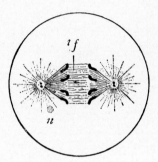

G. The chromosomes are gathered in two groups. The cell wall begins to cave in.

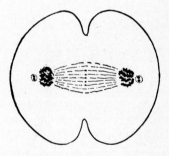

H. The chromosomes have changed into a network of fine threads. A new cell wall has been formed, and the cell division is finished.

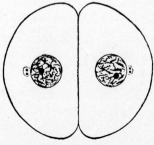

made that organic life can only exist or rather develop
in very few places in the universe; we are living in
one of the favored places, the earth's surface. It is
claimed that this favorable circumstance has enabled
us to live and develop and to think about ourselves
and about the surrounding universe.

We shall now describe some of the characteristic
properties of living matter and organisms of the
forms with which we are familiar. I use here the
term "living matter" for the fundamental elements
out of which "living organisms" are built. What we
describe is life as we *see* it, not life as we feel it—not
the "Life of the Universe," but the physical or space-
time aspect of the type of life that exists on earth.
The study of the characteristics common to all life
will be one of our starting points for a more comprehensive conception of the universe as a whole.

When we study a piece of living matter of the
higher forms the first thing we notice is that it is divided up into small compartments which are called
cells, which in turn are often combined into structures
called *tissues*. The substance of which cells are built
is called *protoplasm*, which has a very complicated
chemical composition. A typical cell consists of a
more or less spherical fluid body called the *nucleus*,

solar system cannot well be explained by the theory that planets
can only be formed when two stars pass one another. Other
theories are proposed which account for the large angular momenta, but they are not yet sufficiently developed.

which is surrounded by a fluid called the *cytoplasm*. The nucleus is sometimes separated from the cytoplasm by a thin membrane, the cell itself is bounded by the *cell wall*, which in fully developed plant cells consists of a relatively heavy and rigid wall of cellulose. The solid parts of cells of plants and animals often partly retain their structure after death as in dry wood, bones or shells and this gives to parts of dead plants and animals a cellular structure, which must not be confused with that of living cells.

Cells are by no means all alike. Certain cells form long fibres while others are flat, and still others are irregular in shape.

All the marvelous structural properties of living matter cannot be here described. The most interesting things about cells are the changes that take place, and it is here that the profound difference between living and non-living matter becomes evident. Living matter *develops* according to certain rules; we shall now study its physical, that is, its structural development in space and time.

If we watch a piece of living tissue in the microscope, we find that certain cells seem unchanging, in others strange changes are taking place, as if unseen agencies were at work. An unchanging cell may after an hour or so become the seat of activities, or it may disintegrate. An unchanging cell is said to be "resting," a disintegrating cell is said to be dying or dead. We can study a living tissue for a long time, only if it is a part of a living animal, or, if not such a part, when we keep it steadily supplied with proper nourishment, keep the temperature at a certain level, prevent germs from entering it, and wash away waste products and disintegration products from dead cells.

We have already mentioned that a cell has a nucleus. During the resting period—which may be short or long and may be prolonged, perhaps indefinitely, by suitable means—the nucleus can be seen to have a structure similar to a fine net, or it appears to contain barely visible and irregularly placed fine threads or small bodies. (Figure I) Usually this structure is colorless and cannot be seen directly in the microscope, but can be made visible by some suitable process of staining.[1] The first thing which marks the end of the resting period in a cell of an animal is that a little "body" appears, or becomes more noticeable, close to the outer wall of the nucleus. This body is called the *centrosome* and possibly originates in the nucleus itself. The centrosome is surrounded by radiating lines and often looks like a little star from which beams radiate in all directions. A close inspection shows that the centrosome has two centers extremely close to one another. As the centrosome moves out into the cyto-

---

[1] The staining usually kills the cell, hence the processes later described cannot be observed in a living cell. The description is an idealized one, derived from a study of many cells in different stages of division.

plasm the two centers separate more and more; the rays which originally appeared as coming from a single center can now be seen to radiate from two well separated points. The separation increases more and more, and sometimes the two centrosomes do not stop moving until they are near the wall of the cell and as far away from one another as they can go within the confines of the cell.

In the meantime an important change takes place in the nucleus itself. The threads in the network become thicker and more noticeable, and they separate finally into a certain definite number of small threads or bodies. These are called *chromosomes* and exist in all living cells, except perhaps in the lowest forms of micro-organisms. Their number is characteristic for the animal or plant we are studying. For example, let us assume that the tissue we are studying comes from an animal with eight chromosomes. A careful examination of the thickening threads in the nucleus before they split up into separate chromosomes might have shown us that the threads were everywhere double. The chromosomes retain this property and at a certain state of the development we are studying—*cell-division* or *mitosis*—we have within the nucleus eight chromosomes, each one consisting of two parallel short threads, or two similarly shaped bodies, placed in close juxtaposition and arranged in an irregular way within the nucleus. The chromosomes often have a spiral structure, but this may partly be due to distortions after they are killed.

As the centrosomes separate, they seem to exert a powerful influence on the group of chromosomes. The latter are set in motion and the nuclear wall bursts. The chromosomes move in a definite way, and finally become lined up in a plate or ring in the plane midway between the two centrosomes. Now the centrosomes begin to exert a pull on the split chromosomes. The pull does not appear to cause simply a widening of the split in the ring, it seems to be a gradual pulling in of the chromosomes toward the two centrosomes, with the force applied at one or several points on each chromosome. We have now sixteen well separated chromosomes, eight moving toward one centrosome, and eight toward the other. When they come very close to the centrosomes a circular constriction develops and becomes deeper and finally a new cell wall is formed in this plane. We have now two cells where we formerly had one.

The new cells usually grow in size till they become about as large as the original one. Then perhaps a short period of rest, or rather of no visible activity—and the newly formed cells are ready for a new division. The tissue of the animal or the plant is *growing*.

It is natural to ask how the complicated process of cell division can be "explained," what is the nature of the mysterious forces involved, what is the mechanism which regulates it, and how a cell can "know" just what to do, when it divides and grows. We shall come to these questions in the next chapter, first we must study more of the marvelous structural developments in living matter.

Since living cells have the property of duplicating themselves, the obvious question is: "How does a plant or an animal start its life?" It was formerly thought that animals were formed from rotting matter, *spontaneous generation* of life was supposed to occur every day. It was not until the latter part of the nineteenth century, after Pasteur's epoch-making experiments, that everybody was convinced that life could only come from life ("omne vivum ex vivo").

Many of the lowest animals and plants—there is hardly any distinction between them—consist of single cells or groups or colonies of cells, which grow by division like the tissue cells we were studying above. All the cells in a group are practically alike and perform the same function, which seems to be simply to obtain nourishment, to grow by division, and ultimately to serve as food for other animals.

In all the higher animals and plants the individual starts its life from a unique cell formed by a junction of two different cells, a *male* and a *female germ cell*. The male germ cell (the terms *sperm cells* and *sperms* will in the following be used) consists of a nucleus with very little cytoplasm, often with a neck and a tail, the latter serving as a means of locomotion. The female germ cell, called *ovum* or *egg cell*, is a larger cell consisting of a nucleus and an abundance of cytoplasm. In birds' eggs the whole yolk is a single cell (ovum), although the active part is restricted to a small mass on one side of the yolk. The rest of the yolk and the "white" outside the ovum serve as food for the developing embryo. The male germ cells have a compact structure of chromosomes and are adapted to mobility, the female cells have a less compact structure of chromosomes, enveloped by cytoplasm containing nourishment. Male and female germ cells have been given the common name *gametes* ("marrying" cells).

The gametes differ from the body cells in an important way. We have said before that the number of chromosomes is characteristic for the cells of an animal or plant. In men the number of chromosomes is 48. If we study human cells from a muscle or from the skin, from the eye or the bones, from the nerves or the brain, if the cell is alive and we can see the chromosomes, it has always 48 of them. The mature germ cells of an animal and of most plants have only half as many chromosomes as the rest of the body. The human ovum and the human sperm cells have 24 chromosomes. The germ cells in animals and most plants are formed by a special kind of cell division (reduction), which it is not necessary to describe here. The important point is that finally half of the chromosomes or their "descendents" go to one cell and the other half to another. (Figure II)

In all animals and higher plants the chromosomes in the body-cells can be arranged in homologous pairs. In the body-cells of many male animals one pair of homologous chromosomes does not consist of identical mates. One of them has the same appearance as the corresponding mates in the female cells, but the other appears to have lost something. The chromosome which appears double in female cells and single in male cells is called the X-chromosome, its apparently incomplete mate in the male cells is called the Y-chromosome. The X-chromosome is also called the *sex chromosome*. When the ova are formed and the number of chromosomes is halved, each of them is left with one X-chromosome. In the formation of sperms half of them contain an X-chromosome, whereas half have a Y-chromosome. The former produce female and the latter male offspring.

In some animals, including birds, the cells in the males have two X-chromosomes, and the cells in the females have one X and one Y. In the reduction process we get then two kinds of egg cells, one with an X- and one with a Y-chromosome, but the sperms have all an X-chromosome. This is just opposite to the case of most mammals, where we have one kind of egg cells and two kinds of sperms.

When reproduction occurs among animals through

FIG. 2.

The Fertilization and First Division of an Ovum.

(By *Bohm* and *von Davidoff*, after *Boveri*.
From *F. R. Bailey*, A TEXTBOOK OF HISTOLOGY
By permission of William Wood and Co., 1917.)

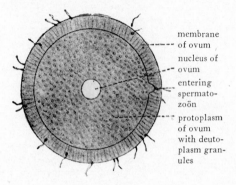

membrane
of ovum

nucleus of
ovum

entering
spermato-
zoön

protoplasm
of ovum
with deuto-
plasm gran-
ules

1. The nucleus is shown in the center as a transparent spot. The ovum is surrounded by sperm cells, one of which is in the act of penetration.

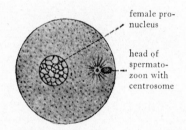

female pro-
nucleus

head of
spermato-
zoon with
centrosome

2. The threads in the nucleus begin to be visible. The head of the sperm cell has entered the cytoplasm, and the centrosome is seen near the sperm cell.

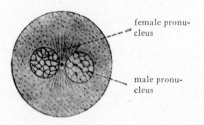

female pronu-
cleus

male pronu-
cleus

3. The sperm cell has expanded greatly and its structure is visible. The rays of the centrosomes are developing.

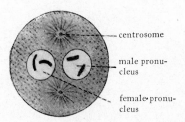

centrosome

male pronu-
cleus

female pronu-
cleus

4. The chromosomes are visible, two from the ovum and two from the sperm cell. The centrosome has split and its components have moved away from one another.

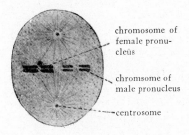

chromosome of
female pronu-
cleus

chromsome of
male pronucleus

centrosome

5. The chromosomes are split and begin to separate.

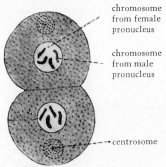

chromosome
from female
pronucleus

chromosome
from male
pronucleus

centrosome

6. The cell division is finished. The ovum and the sperm cell have made equal contributions to the two chromosome systems.

a union of a male and female germ cell, the small mobile sperm travels to the larger egg cell, which has a stored supply of nourishment. The first sperm which comes in contact with an egg cell starts a development of the egg cell, hence, on the average, half the fertilized eggs become females and half become males. The fertilized egg immediately begins to divide in the same way as do ordinary cells, a process which has earlier been described.

To understand the nature of life in general we must follow the development of an individual organism. Let us first take one of the lowliest forms, yeast, for instance. It is a plant, or rather a colony of fungi, each of which multiplies by budding. These cells obtain their oxygen from sugar manufactured by other plants, and they are very abundant in fruit and fruit juices, in which they cause fermentation. This consists in the splitting up of sugar into alcohol and the gas carbon dioxide, a fact which has led to the use of yeast for making dough swell up, which occurs when the cellular activities are increased by heat and moisture.

The yeast cells have nuclei (although they cannot be seen without staining and killing the cell), cytoplasm and cell walls, in no way different from the cells of higher organisms on earth, and the nuclei have a very simple set of chromosomes. In the cytoplasm of the cells is a complicated chemical substance called *zymase*, which belongs to a class of active substances called *enzymes* or *ferments*. Enzymes have the property of breaking up complicated chemical substances into simpler ones, and they play an important role in the digestion of the food in animals and plants. That zymase is not a living substance can be seen from the fact that it can be extracted even from dead cells and, when brought into a sugar solution, can produce all the effects of fermentation. This process must therefore be a secondary chemical one not directly dependent upon life.

We shall now study the development of an organism of a higher type.[1] The development of man, so far as the physical aspect is concerned, is very similar to that of other mammals, no qualitative difference has ever been established.

We described before the union of an egg cell and a sperm. But a father is not quite necessary, even among organisms which normally have sexual reproduction. For instance, if we take non-fertilized eggs of silk worms and brush them vigorously, some of them will develop normally (artificial *parthenogenesis*). The same thing can be accomplished by chemical or other mechanical means. It may well be that the ovum simply receives an electric shock, and

[1] The following description of embryonic development is derived from amphibia and is of necessity very schematic. The development in the higher vertebrates and the mammals differs somewhat from the description here given, but not in any way which would in the least weaken the force of the arguments in the subsequent chapters.

this causes a splitting of the chromosomes, a phenomenon which we shall discuss further in the next chapter. The ovum divides into two similar cells, each one divides again, and this process goes on until a little ball of cells, called a *morula* ("mulberry") has been formed. Due to internal accumulation of water this sphere expands and becomes hollow and we have what is called a *blastula*. (Figure III) The thick lower part [1] of the blastula, called the "vegetative" half, consists of large cells rich in yolk; the thin upper part, the "animal" half, is composed of numerous small cells poor in yolk and the transition zone consists of medium sized cells. In the vegetative half is a spot (first noticed in 1920 by O. Mangold on blastulas without any membrane) which seems to play a very important role in the future development.

In the blastulas of *animals* a strange and mysterious transformation takes place. At the spot mentioned a little depression appears, and the vegetative half begins to move into the cavity. At the lower boundary of the transition zone the cells are turned sharply inwards and the sharp turning produces a well defined "ring." The cells in the blastula begin to stretch and contract, evidently under the influence of a concerted field of force. All the cells in the

[1] Terms like upper and lower, dorsal and ventral refer to positions relative to the fully developed animal with its head up and its tail down.

vegetative half enter into the cavity. The ring contracts until it forms a narrow opening or slit, which is called the *blastopore*. At its dorsal lip the movements are most rapid, and here cells often temporarily pile up and form a protuberance. The whole transition zone is finally forced through the narrow opening into the cavity. The vegetative half is now spread out in the interior and is called the *entoderm*. The transition zone becomes the *mesoderm*, and it was so sharply turned back at the edge of the blastopore that it forms a layer in contact with the *inside* of the outer wall, which is now called the *ectoderm*. The mesoderm which has passed the dorsal lip extends farther up into the cavity than that which has passed the ventral lip. The embryo is now called a *gastrula*, and some animals like the simplest coelenterates do not develop beyond this stage.

In the higher animals after the gastrula stage is reached nerve tissue begins to form in the ectoderm, but only in those regions which are underlaid by the mesoderm which has passed the dorsal lip. A "neural plate" is thus formed, its edges are turned up and form a tube which sinks into the mesoderm beneath. This tube is the beginning of the nerve system and is characteristic for all vertebrates. It is important to note that the brain develops in the upper end of the tube which originates in the mesoderm cells which first passed the dorsal lip, and the spinal cord and the central nervous system grow from the cells which afterwards pass this point. The ectoderm becomes the covering and the outer parts of the body, the entoderm produces the digestive tract.

Something in the dorsal lip of the blastopore is responsible for the organization both of the animal as a whole and of its parts. This region is hence sometimes referred to as a "center of organization." For our later investigations it is important to note that the cells are moving past this region, and that organization hence is induced at a fixed place in which the individual cells and atoms are steadily replaced by new ones.

There is other evidence that something of fundamental importance is emanating from the edge of the blastopore. Some years ago Spemann and Hilde Mangold transplanted material from the center of the dorsal lip of a gastrula to the ventral surface of another gastrula having a different coloration, and the cells from the two gastrulas could hence be distinguished from one another. The transplanted piece followed the flow of cells through the blastopore and lodged on the inner, ventral side. Then it developed like a complete gastrula and formed its own mesoderm, and in the adjacent ectoderm a neural plate was formed. An apparently complete secondary embryo developed on the ventral side of the principal one. The development of the "host" was not much disturbed, although it furnished the building material for both embryos.

Many biologists have since extensively studied such phenomena and have found that the organization is progressive. At an early stage cells can develop into complete embryos, later their development has been fixed in a general way, still later in a more special way, and in the end no further specialization of cells occurs.[1] For instance, transplantation experiments show that a cell group can at a certain stage develop into a complete head, or into any part of a head, later it can only develop into a mouth, or any part of a mouth, and so on. When the development is once started it seems to go on automatically. If we displace a developing eye lens, a new eye lens is formed in its proper position, and we can form several new eye lenses even if the original one is developing properly.

Many animals and particularly the insects undergo complete changes of form, *metamorphosis*. First we have the fertilized egg from which a larva develops. The larva is the feeding and growing state, then comes a "resting" period, when the insect is in the form of a pupa. In this stage a wonderful development takes place, very similar to an embryonic development, the difference being simply that the

[1] The organization is not irrevocably fixed, however. Before a particular stage is reached, seemingly defined at the time of formation of neurones, the development of a part of an embryo can be altered by being transplanted into another region of the embryo. If no stable neurones are formed the organization can probably be reversed and altered at any time. Cf. page 109.

building material is stored in the body of the larva and not received from a mother. When the development is completed, the larva is gone, and a full grown insect, perhaps a beautiful butterfly, emerges from the "grave" to live a short, perhaps happy life and reproduce itself—and then comes death and disintegration.

The process which regulates the development in the pupa state is the same as that which regulates the development of an animal or human embryo. From somewhere in the body of the larva a "wave" emanates, it spreads to the whole body and activates successively new and hitherto hidden potentialities in the cells of the larva. The cells change their appearance, some become the hard shell of the insect, others become the multiple eyes, others the nervous system and others the wings and the legs.

We shall later return to this "wave of organization," which can change a larva to a butterfly. It is not material, that is, it is not built of atoms. It represents a type of structure which is of great importance in the present study.

Let us go back to the embryo. The wave of organization has spread from the blastopore and reached all parts of the gastrula. Membranes begin to develop, vessels carrying nourishing blood and connected with the circulatory system of the mother are formed. The head begins to develop and the beginning of a spinal column becomes visible. The eyes develop early: the cornea, the eye lens and the vitreous humor from the skin; and the optic cup, the retina and the optic nerve from brain substance. Gill slits appear and disappear later in the development of the mammals, but are retained in fish embryos. Arms or legs are appearing, the five fingers and toes are coming out like buds, and the characteristic features of the animal become more and more pronounced.

The organizing agency has a tremendous work on hand; it must build up a heart and a circulatory system, a skeleton and a skull, organs of sight and hearing, a nervous system and a brain, and attend to the billions of small things which are necessary for a satisfactory functioning and coordination of the organism. Then the foetus is ready for birth, it is ready to live an independent life, find its own food, perceive the outside world, develop its own mind, accumulate memories, think and act, sometimes wisely and sometimes foolishly, acquire an ego ("soul")— and finally a change takes place which we call *Death*.

We shall not continue the physical description of living matter and living organisms beyond this point. Much more could be said, but it would be a variation of the general theme we have outlined. We have emphasized the marvelous uniformity of all life and disregarded the equally marvelous diversity of life on earth, although the latter will also serve as an important datum in our later deductions.

FIG. 3.

*Development of a Gastrula
in an Amphibian Egg.*

(From *Hans Spemann*, EMBRYONIC DEVELOPMENT AND INDUCTION. Yale University Press, 1938.)

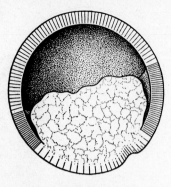

A. A blastula has developed from the fertilized egg cell. The upper wall (the animal half) consists of small cells poor in yolk, the lower portion (the vegetative half) consists of larger cells rich in yolk, and between them is a transition zone of medium sized cells. The cavity of the cell is partly filled with cells rich in yolk belonging to the vegetative portion. On the bottom side is a little depression which later develops into the blastopore.

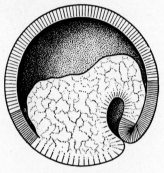

B. The animal half has extended downwards, the blastopore has developed and at its dorsal edge the transition zone is being turned into the cavity.

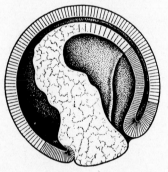

C. The vegetative cells have moved up into the cavity, the transition zone has partly passed the dorsal edge and has begun to move in at the ventral edge.

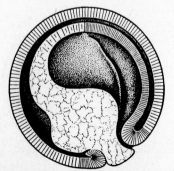

D. Nearly the whole transition zone has moved into the cavity and now forms the mesoderm. The animal half is at the outside of the gastrula and forms the ectoderm. The vegetative portion forms the entoderm.

E. The vegetative half and the transition zone have completely moved into the cavity, and the gastrulation is finished.

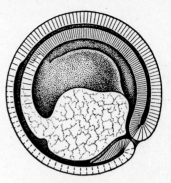

F. This shows another section of the gastrula with the dorsal mesoderm beneath the top layer. The growth of nerve tissue begins in the ectoderm adjacent to the dorsal mesoderm.

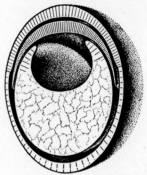

G. The neural plate is shown as a shield extending from the blastopore at the bottom over the dorsal side to the top where it widens out and later develops into the brain. The edges of the neural plate are turned up and then fold in and form the neural tube.

H. A section across the neural tube.

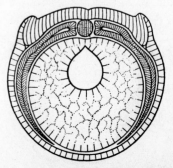

CHAPTER 6

The Mechanical Aspect
of Life

FOR PRIMITIVE man everything in nature appeared either as a friend or an enemy. He had unceasingly to fight wild animals and occasionally his fellowmen; and the fighting spirit in his "blood" still exists in a potential form in many men and in nearly all animals. He loved his friends and hated his enemies. There were good and evil "spirits" in the world. The warming sun was a good spirit which he worshipped, the lightning was an evil spirit, which struck terror to his heart. As he began to investigate things and phenomena more closely, he found that there were *rules* regulating natural phenomena, and his terror for the unknown gradually diminished. The first rules he found were rather special, but his race was so persistent in studying nature that the general rules governing gravity, inertia, and electricity were discovered and applied in his tools and later in his machinery and his instruments. Life, death, and mentality were still mysteries to him, but so far as matter, motion and radiation were concerned, he thought he knew practically everything that could be known.   With this familiarity came a certain contempt for matter, since it did not act in any unexpected way—when he kicked a stone it did not strike back at him as many animals did.

With the discovery of the properties of "empty" space and of the atomic structure of matter and of action, our respect for matter and empty space has been partly restored.   Matter has still no terror for us, however, except when the atoms are in rapid motion (heat), or the radiation is intense enough to burn us.   The whole material universe seems to have originated in a somewhat mysterious fashion, but it appears to be ruled by simple mathematical laws, which, with some modifications, can probably be extended even to the internal structure of atomic nuclei and to electrons.   The material world looks like one of our machines, in which one wheel drives another. We are baffled, however, when we reach the more fundamental entities, their cause, mode of action, and structure in space and time.   The significance of matter is beyond our comprehension, although philosophers and physicists have made great strides toward an understanding of the external world and its relation to the human mind.   Our power of deduction has increased with our knowledge of natural phenomena.   Our efforts of *generalizations* have been particularly successful, which indicates that nature in spite of her apparent diversity is in reality wonderfully uniform.

It was formerly thought that life processes could not be explained by the operation of known physical and chemical forces. Many strange substances were produced in living organisms, which apparently could not be made in the test tubes of the chemical laboratory, and unknown forces were supposed to be responsible for their production. In 1828 Wöhler was able to produce a typical organic substance, *urea*, from inorganic matter, and then came the great advance in organic chemistry. One after another of the less complicated organic substances was produced (synthesized) in the laboratories, but the more complicated substances, like the proteins in the muscles and in the "white" of eggs, the haemoglobin in the red blood corpuscles, and the basic cell-substance, protoplasm, have resisted all attempts at synthetic production, though in some cases fairly good imitations can be produced. Growing cell structures can be imitated, but there are obviously no chromosomes and no real reproduction. Most people believe that part of the phenomena in living organisms can be accounted for by "ordinary" physical and chemical forces, but that at some state in the process new agencies may be at work. The *mechanists* in biology maintain that the new agencies can be simply explained when we know a little more about physics; life for them is an interesting playground of molecular structures, fundamentally due to electric forces. Since atoms in general seem to come together according to the laws of chance, life might be due to chance combinations of atoms and the play of "blind" forces.

The *vitalists* maintain that undoubtedly known physical forces are at work in the processes of life, but that at a certain state recourse must be taken to a new mysterious agency, a "vital force," a "drive towards perfection," an "élan vital," before the secrets of life can be satisfactorily explained.

Other people regard life as "created" or "animated" by some almighty power which they call *God*, the creator and the organizer of the universe. The knowledge of God and his work is not derived from observations, but from individual intuition, and particularly from "revelations" given by one or more wise or holy men to humanity. In some religions God has only made the rules and started the processes in the universe, in others he guides and supervises every detail (Divine Providence).

The vitalists occupy a middle position among the groups mentioned, since the vital force is supernatural and may be ascribed to a direct or indirect action of a God, whose actions transcend natural forces.

In this book arguments will be given to show that all three positions are equally valid and that their advocates use different languages and see or conceive different aspects of a common world.

We shall now study life from the standpoint of physics to see if it is possible to explain all the phenomena of life by mechanical laws. Since we have no assurance that all physical laws have already been discovered, it is permissible to add new rules to this science. These must not be arbitrary, however, for then any kind of assumption could be made. They must always be justified by analogies; in other words, they must be generalizations of known rules and of the same type, therefore expressible in terms of space and time. Since gravity between the small elements we are studying may be disregarded and since we study life mainly as it is revealed by light waves, that is, by electro-magnetic radiation, our rules must be expressed in terms of electric structures differing in space and varying in time, on both a small and a large scale. We must be satisfied with general analogies. The generalizations may appear reasonable or not, but with the present highly developed laboratory technic it should not be very difficult to verify some of the assumptions made.

At this point a few words must be said about water and of a state of matter, the *colloidal state*, a subject not hitherto mentioned. As we all know water is a combination of two atoms of hydrogen and one atom of oxygen, and watervapor consists of molecules of this composition. Water in the liquid form, however, is much more complex; it has been found to be a mixture of "active" and "inactive" groups of atoms.

An active group may be compared to a little bar or crystal, carrying a positive electric charge on one end and a negative charge on the other, it is called a "polar molecule." Other substances, like kerosene and oil, consist of "non-polar molecules," which we may regard as groups of electric charges in which the positive and negative elements are "joining hands," thus neutralizing each other. Sugar in solution is a relatively large molecule with electric charges sticking out at its sides, capable of catching other polar molecules. The moving polar molecules of water exert a pull on the sides of the sugar molecules in a lump of sugar and quickly tear the lump to pieces, and the sugar is "dissolved." If the water is hot, the molecules of water move with greater speed, and sugar is hence dissolved more quickly in warm than in cold water. The non-polar molecules of oil can not disrupt sugar, since they exert no pull.

A body like soap has molecules which are neutral at one end and have an electric charge at the other. Soap molecules float in water with their charged ends down and their neutral ends up and tend to spread out over the surface in a film of uniform thickness. The strength of a soap bubble is due to this property, and its iridescence to the fact that the very thin uniform films of soap molecules spread light of different colors in different but definite directions (diffraction). Soap molecules float in oil with their neutral ends down and their active ends up.

Water will not mix with oil, since one has polar molecules, the other non-polar. If we add a little soap to the mixture and shake it well, the oil will be spread out in the water in the form of globules, and we get an *emulsion* of oil in water. The soap molecules are at the surface of the oil drops, their neutral ends sticking down into the electrically neutral oil, and their charged ends sticking out into the water with its polar molecules. If the oil drops are very small we speak of a *colloidal solution* in water, and the oil is said to be in a *"colloidal state."*

In the colloidal state of matter we can have very large electric charges on the surface, that is, the charges are large in proportion to the weight or mass of the drops. The drops are therefore easily moved by electric forces and act like strongly electrified bodies in an electric field. There can be little doubt that parts of the protoplasm and the proteins in the cytoplasm and in the nucleus of a cell are in a colloidal state, that is, this matter is suspended as small bodies or rather drops having high electric charges, distributed in the interior and over the surface in a way dependent upon the nature of the particular protein.

In a previous chapter we said that the physical universe has a "particle aspect" and a "wave aspect," and we spoke about guiding fields and guiding waves as "immaterial" structures in space-time and of "material" particles as entities in which the energy was in a very concentrated form. Atoms were regarded as consisting of material elements—neutrons, positrons, and electrons—cemented together and organized by an immaterial space-time structure with fine "meshes" or "cells" defined by the quantum of action, a structure which in modern physics is regarded as the substratum that organizes and inflates atoms, molecules, crystals, and solid bodies in general. Matter owes some of its structural properties to the *field* in which the particles of matter are embedded, and this field guides the particles in space and time and affects their spacing and sometimes also their configurations. Pilot waves appear to govern the motions of electrons; the electrons do not govern the motions of pilot waves. It is necessary to assume that the *immaterial wave system governs the position and motion of the material elements, and not vice versa.* The removal of an electron from an atom, for instance, is here supposed to be the effect rather than the cause of a change in the immaterial structure. In short, the material structure follows the changes in the immaterial structure and is determined by the latter.

The immaterial structure of an atom or a crystal has no observable existence in the absence of material particles. In spite of the fact that this structure seems to define the position and motion of particles, we have no means of deciding whether this kind of structure has an independent existence or not. When a crystal is dissolved in a liquid, for example, the immaterial structure that builds up the crystal dissolves into the more elementary parts which give the individual molecules their structural characteristics. But the existence of certain immaterial structures must be postulated even in the absence of material elements. For instance, radio waves on which the human voice has been impressed must have a structure in space and time that represents the sound vibrations. The electro-magnetic waves are caused by moving electrons but the waves themselves carry no electrons and travel in empty space with the velocity of light. When they strike the antennae of our radio receivers, they set electrons in motion, the resulting electric currents are amplified and act in our loud-speakers, and the structure carried is revealed to us as the sound of a voice. It is important to note that such space-time structures can only become observable when they interact or are in association with material particles.

We have said that it is the guiding field and the guiding waves which determine the motions and relative positions of particles. In the living world, with its marvelous structures, changes, and specific functions, the need for guiding space-time structures is even more urgent than in the inorganic world. Observations show that it is necessary to postulate the existence of certain factors with space and time properties as carriers of the structural characteristics.

These carriers must in general be very stable, since they must convey the hereditary structural properties through a long series of generations. They must be much more complex and diversified than the structures exhibited by atoms, molecules and crystals. Although stable they must be capable of undergoing certain changes which will later be studied. They must themselves be *immaterial*, but they must be capable of defining within certain limits the positions and motions of special kinds of molecules, and they should hence appear to us as a field of force with an extremely complex inner structure. The new structures we introduce should not be regarded as identical with those generally assumed to exist in inorganic matter and in the radio waves just considered. What part the quantum of action may play in the new type of structure is not clear; evidently a great number of factors of which we have no direct knowledge are reflected in the structure. The most characteristic thing about it is that *it must to a great extent be independent of the incorporated material elements*.

A field of force can not exist without sustaining *sources*. In an electric field the sources are the electrons and the atomic nuclei, in a gravitational field the sources are in the atoms (probably in the neutrons). In radiation the sources may be represented by the photons which must be regarded as *immaterial* because their rest mass is zero. In a "living" wave system the sources are much more complex than those defining the non-living wave systems. From the living sources springs the essence of the living wave systems, and without the sustaining sources the wave systems would quickly be dissipated. The living sources are duplicated in cell division, hence they can not carry any mass and energy since the principle of conservation of mass and energy would then be violated. Living sources must hence be regarded as *immaterial,* and they are characterized by many properties some of which we shall later describe. We may think of them as mass-free entities similar to photons or neutrinos. As with sources in general, their energy, dimension, structure, position and motion are definable only by their associated wave systems. Some of the properties of the sources "emerge" in the wave systems (that is, in space-time) in the form of frequency and energy patterns observable as fields of force having a structure of a more complex type than that of atoms in which the sources are the centers of electrical and gravitational force fields. Energy can be imparted to and removed from a living wave system by certain non-living substances (hormones). The radius of action of such a wave system increases with its energy content and becomes practically zero when all the energy is lost.

We are here concerned only with the space-time aspect of these strange structures, that is, we study only the play of shadows cast in our consciousness by the living organisms around us. Can we learn anything at all about the origin and inherent nature of the mysterious sources which are responsible for the essential qualities of the wave systems and according to the picture previously presented emerge from a world beyond space and time? We shall come to this problem later.

We shall now make the following assertions. Living organisms consist of combinations of special kinds of molecules and special immaterial space-time structures (wave systems) which latter define the motions, position and vibration periods of electric charges. The molecular structures and the wave systems must have a certain degree of correspondence in order to remain in association. If the immaterial structure is not associated with molecules in all of its "cells," it can capture and incorporate additional molecules of proper structure, provided these molecules move with sufficiently small velocities.

In the following we shall find many reasons for making these assumptions. In the first place we can now picture the building up of complex proteins in living cells. Proteins from dead animals or plants are eaten and split up into amino-acids by the enzymes in the digestive organs. The amino-acids are carried by the blood stream into the fine capillaries which exist everywhere in the body. The lymph which is seeping through all the tissues carries the amino-acids to the walls of all the cells, and the amino-acids can penetrate the cell walls and enter the cytoplasm in every living cell.

Within every living cell we assume that there are many special immaterial fine-structures, which can "capture" the amino-acids and combine them into complex proteins of a structure somewhat similar to the special immaterial structures in the particular cells. We know that complex fluid structures, when unaided by any special organizing agency, in general decompose and can only remain unchanged by being kept at such a low temperature that they are permanently frozen. Special "organizers" are needed to build up complex structures of special properties; in inorganic nature where the organizers are of a simple type the tendency is toward a much simpler kind of organization (as in molecules and crystals), and toward the greatest possible degree of disorganization in the aggregate of smaller units (as in the case of diffusion in liquids and gases). The development in the organic world is toward complexity instead of simplicity and toward special organization of the smaller units instead of their haphazard disorganization.

To illustrate the effect of temperature consider a sperm cell with its chromosomes. It has an internal structure with a complexity far beyond our comprehension, and according to our hypothesis it is the *immaterial, living* structure which is primarily responsible for this complexity. The protein molecules are combined with water and form a fluid structure which fits into the living structure. Goetz and others have recently found that if yeast cells or sperm cells are cooled to the temperature of liquid hydrogen they can remain alive, provided the cooling is so rapid that the crystallization near the freezing point of water is avoided. At such low temperatures all the activities of the cell are suspended. It seems that the time dimension in its space-time structure has practically disappeared, and that the cell's intrinsic time stands almost still. The electrons can move, but not the molecules. That the cell is still alive can be shown by heating it to room temperature, when it again acquires its normal properties. This heating must again be so rapid that the cell quickly passes through the critical temperature of crystallization or devitrification.

When the cell is still fluid there is a certain degree of correspondence between the living and the non-living wave systems, because the molecules have originally been properly arranged to fit the living structure. When the temperature reaches the freezing point for the fluid, the molecules tend to congeal and form crystals, which is the normal state for inorganic solid bodies. This rearrangement of the molecules into crystals takes time, however; it is rapid at the temperature of freezing, slower at a lower temperature, and infinitely slow at the absolute zero. Under ordinary conditions if the living structure can not keep each individual molecule at its proper place and vibration, it can at least keep the system of molecules in proper order, provided the molecules do not move or oscillate too fast, as they do at very high temperatures. The crystalline state, however, can not be made to correspond to the living immaterial structure, probably because "connections" or "electric bonds" would then exist, which are incompatible with the living wave system. For the cell to remain alive it is hence essential that the development of crystals be prevented, and this is accomplished in these experiments by making the speed of molecular rearrangement, reorientation and vibrations infinitely slow.

The chromosomes are extremely important parts of the living cells. In the next chapter we shall see why they must be regarded as built up of smaller units called *genes*, which in the gemetes carry the elementary hereditary characters of animals and plants and in the body cells many of the specific properties in a potential form.

We shall assume that one of the effects of the immaterial fine-structures in growing tissues is the production of genes, which are here regarded as colloidal proteins organized by and combined with special elementary units of the immaterial, living structure. Most of the genes are in the chromosomes which can be regarded as strings of genes. We shall later give reasons for the belief that also in the cytoplasm of the cells there is a complex structure which carries some of the potentialities of life and certain hereditary characters.

We shall now consider a possible explanation of cell division in ordinary physical terms,[1] provided we are permitted to introduce special immaterial living structures into the genes and to make some further generalizations of physical laws.

The primary cause of cell-division may be simply an electric charge, transmitted to the living chromosomes in the nucleus. This suggestion was made before in connection with the description of artificial parthenogenesis. If an electric charge is the cause of the first division of the ovum, we may assume that the same is the case for the division of body cells. When the charge, whether positive, negative, or complex, we do not know, reaches the living chromosomes, they are split into two parts which are ordinarily entirely identical. We have no very good analogy to this in atomic physics. The nearest one appears to be the phenomenon of ionization, which may be described in the following way. Energy is imparted to an atom and the disturbance causes the ejection of an electron and its pilot waves. The immaterial structure is this "split" into two parts, one part carrying the ejected electron and the other carrying the nucleus and the rest of the electrons.

[1] A more profound theory is given on p. 156 f.

Though the split parts are not alike in this case the phenomena of ionization of atoms and of splitting of chromosomes and genes are probably of similar nature.[1] We have reason to assume that it is the non-material structure in the chromosomes and not the amino-acid molecules which is split into two parts. The material elements follow the changes in the immaterial structure, as is the case of the ionization of atoms. If the material structure can not do this, the chromosome "dies."

The complex electric charges are probably the same in the two components of the split chromosomes, because they seem to repel one another and because the resultant elements are in most cases completely alike.

One pair of elements exerts a strong repelling force on one another. They are the centrosomes, of which we have spoken before. In some cases they seem to originate in the nucleus and break through the nuclear wall and move toward the cell wall, as far away from one another as they can possibly go within the cell. When they have taken up their position, they regulate the motions of the chromosomes, seemingly by hydrodynamic forces acting along the

---

[1] One reason why atoms are not split into two equal parts is due to the fact that much less energy is required to "split" the atomic atmosphere than to "split" the atomic nucleus. The dissociation of a diatomic gas into a monatomic one offers a case where the two split parts are alike, but they are not equivalent to the original molecules, and the splitting can hence not proceed further.

"rays," the origin and nature of which will be discussed in another connection. At first the centrosomes seem to repel the chromosomes and force them into the equatorial plane. After the chromosomes have been definitely oriented and the separation of the two components of the chromosomes has reached a certain stage, the rays seem to contract, and they exert a pull at one or more definite points on the chromosomes, another indication of a differentiation of charge along these bodies. The half chromosomes are gathered together in the respective regions near the two centrosomes, additional amino-acids are incorporated in the non-material structures, precipitated as proteins on the cell wall and in the plane between the two nuclei, where a new cell wall is formed —and the cell division is finished.

The fertilization and first division of the ovum may be described in the same way as the division of a body cell. The chromosomes in the sperm as well as the chromosomes in the nucleus of the ovum are split by the electric disturbance. The charge was apparently carried on the surface of the "head" of the sperm, which superficially may be regarded as similar to a colloidal speck of protein suspended in water.

The equal distribution of split chromosomes from the sperm and the ovum in the first division is probably due to analogous distribution of electric charges along the homologous chromosomes.

The development of the ovum into a morula is

mainly a repeated division. The development into a blastula with its vegetative and animal regions centered about an incipient blastopore is the first indication that the animal is destined to become a single organized being. The material of which the gastrula is built is as fluid as the yolk of a hen's egg, it consists of a mass of moving fluid cells. It has some superficial similarity to a vortex ring, but transplantation experiments show that the movements are not "caused" by the circulation at the blastopore. If we think of the motions as regulated by a "vortex system," the *whole* blastula and the *whole* gastrula are parts of such a system. The thing that defines the blastopore can not be "matter" of any known type, for any kind of fluid matter would be carried along with the moving material or would simply rotate at the sharp edge. Neither can it be a vortex system regulated by ordinary mechanical or electrical forces.

Here we have a simple and yet striking example of a living immaterial structure or wave system. A "field" or a "wave system" regulates the motions of atoms, it has intricate properties which atoms as such do not seem to have, and it is not itself permanently associated with any atoms. The gastrula stage is only a preliminary step in the development. The permanent organization is transferred to the moving cells as they are forced through the slit of the blastopore. The structure and functions of a vertebrate animal are, however, regulated by the central nervous system, which is centered in the brain and the spinal chord. Hence the edges of the slit should not be equivalent; the dorsal edge should be the main center of organization, and this is just what we find. Somewhere in the dorsal lip is the very center of organization; a center which transmits to the passing cells in succession the potentialities of becoming a head, a trunk, and a tail, and makes possible the formation of a complete, highly organized animal. In this process the structure of the complete animal is, in expanded but still latent form, transferred to that portion of the mesoderm in which the growth of nerve tissue begins.

For such an important "potentiality" or "structure" as this organizing entity evidently is, we need a name. It is sometimes called an "organizing field," and we have previously called this entity a "wave of organization," but we shall in the following use the term *genie*,[1] a word which sounds sufficiently mysterious and suggests a relationship with genes. The name also suggests a wisdom far beyond our comprehension.

What is then a genie? There are many types of genii, some are special, others more general. Of the

[1] The word genie comes from the Latin word *genius* (spirit), the plural form *genii* has in English been given the singular form genie (French, génie) as equivalent to the Arabic word *jinni*, which is the name of the spirits described in the Arabian Nights. The word gene, on the other hand, comes from the Greek word *genos* (family, race).

general genii, one determines the general structure of the human organism, another the structure of a dog, another of a larva, another of the butterfly developing from the larva. Of the special or subordinate genii, one determines the structure and activities of the heart, another the structure of the eye, and so on.

When an egg cell first divides, the gene system in the chromosomes is distributed equally between the two daughter cells. Sometimes the system of genii is also split and this results in the formation of identical twins. Now it is extremely difficult to understand how such a complex wave system as a genie apparently is can be split into two parts of which each one is equivalent to the common parent. In a later chapter some arguments and facts will be given which indicate that during the splitting of genes and genii their wave systems do not interact with atoms and probably are in a highly contracted form, perhaps even contracted to such an extent that our ordinary conception of space extension has no counterpart in the external world. An equivalent way of expressing it is to say that it is the *sources* which are first split, and that this splitting does not take place in space-time. It involves *all* the properties of the genes and genii, not only their physical attributes.

The wave system which determines the motions in the gastrula is here regarded as due to a particular genie, the *gastrula genie*, which is one of the subordinate genii but expands before the other genii.   Its structure in space and time determines how the cells shall move in relation to the blastopore.   If a morula is constricted so that it forms two more or less separated halfs, which can be done without killing the cells, the future fate of the two halfs depends upon the orientation of the constriction in relation to the gastrula genie.   If the constriction is in a frontal plane we can get a dorsal and a ventral part, of which the dorsal part contains the center of organization and develops into a complete embryo and the ventral half develops into a round piece without differentiation.   If the constriction is in a median plane, two *half embryos* are formed, which are exactly alike but one represents the left and the other the right half of the animal.   The first cleavage plane of the egg cell often coincides with the median plane, indicating that the gastrula genie begins its expansion immediately after the fertilization and can very early exert its influence on the motions.   If the constriction is made in this plane the future development has perfect bilateral symmetry relative to it, and two half embryos are formed.   The surprising fact is found, however, that if the constriction is deep and if the cells are shaken up, the half embryos develop into complete ones.   The same happens if the two halfs are completely separated.   If no constriction is made but one of the two first daughter cells is killed, the other cell develops into a half embryo.   If the killed daughter cell is removed, however, a complete embryo develops from the living cell. These strange facts can now be understood. The right and left expansions of the general genie in a vertebrate animal are not in themselves stable wave systems. They can retain their structure only if they are intimately associated with the proper kind of molecules arranged in a certain pattern. If this pattern is upset by shaking the fluid mass, or even by simply upsetting the stratification due to gravity, the two asymmetric wave systems revert to symmetrical ones which then reorganize the matter and produce complete embryos. Often this rearrangement is incomplete, particularly at a later stage when the association with atoms has become more rigidly fixed, but the tendency is definitely in the direction of completion.

This process of *restitution* of fractional wave systems into complete ones shows clearly the integral character of the general genie. It indicates that when a living wave system can freely adjust itself in response to abnormal conditions which we should expect to cause its division, it reacts on the *source* and may cause a splitting of the source itself, which is coextensive with the wave system. This splitting is sometimes only partial, as evidenced by the formation of double heads or tails. The phenomenon is of the same nature as the splitting of genes and genii in the formation of gametes, the production of which must be regarded as due to "mechanical" causes acting

on the living wave systems and through them on the
sources, which then develop double wave systems
which in their turn rearrange the molecules and
form double structures. (Cf. p. 156 f.).

The gastrula genie is an important, living wave
system which changes with time. It interacts to
some extent with the matter in the gastrula which re-
flects the gross features of the changing structure.
The general genie and the rest of the subordinate
genii, on the other hand, do not in the first stages of
development interact with matter. They remain
centered at a fixed place which we, using terms bor-
rowed from hydrodynamics, would designate as a
"stagnation point in the gastrula vortex," which place
is near or at the dorsal lip of the blastopore. At the
time of invagination the genii, which themselves are
immaterial, living "sources," absorb energy and begin
to develop their wave systems which then interact
with the atoms in the neighborhood, and certain important chemical substances (hormones) are formed
during this process. On account of the interaction
with matter the system of genii can no longer be kept
in place but is carried "head" first by the cell flow in
the immediate neighborhood of the stagnation point
and lodges with the head in front in the dorsal mesoderm.[1] The hormones are also carried along and

---

[1] The genii, both in their developed and undeveloped form,
have a fixed space-time relation to one another and form an
integral system coordinated by the general genie. The bond

cause expansion of the genii, and at the same time the interaction with matter becomes more and more general. The result of this expansion and interaction is a special progressive rearrangement of molecules which we observe as a growth of nerve tissue in the dorsal mesoderm and the adjacent ectoderm. The different subordinate genii expand in a certain order and gradually become "fixed" or "materialized." The organization can then ordinarily no longer be modified or reversed, but there are cases as we shall see later when the interlocking between the living wave systems around the genii and the "matter waves," that is, the non-living wave systems in the atoms, is so loose that reorganization is possible.

Before we proceed we must more fully describe a very important element in the mechanism of the development of living cells. We have said that all the cells in a plant or animal have the same chromosomes and the same genes. A gene is only a *potentiality*, however, and to change this potentiality into an actuality something is needed, which is called a *hormone* (from the Greek word *hormao*, I arouse to activity). Hormones are usually defined as chemical substances, which in animals are secreted by ductless glands in the blood stream and activate special or-

between the genii and the matter in the egg cell, the morula and the early gastrula is through the gastrula genie, which interacts with the matter in the embryo until the system of genii is transferred to the mesoderm. The gastrula genie then contracts and looses its control over the future development.

gans.   There are many kinds of hormones, some stimulate growth, others stimulate activities of different kinds.   Although there is no direct evidence that hormones act on special genes, such an assumption is necessary if we use a more general conception of hormones.   We shall regard hormones as being always necessary for the activation and development of genes and genii.   We shall hence generalize the concept of a hormone to include all kinds of impulses necessary for the special development of tissues (differentiation).   A hormone can thus be a chemical substance, a nerve impulse, or an electric "wave" of special properties.   But we shall throughout regard hormones as *non-living* structures, that is, substances in which the sources and their wave systems are not produced by a process of splitting.[1]

When a living wave system interacts with matter in colloidal form it tends to arrange the atoms in certain space-time patterns similar to its own.   The first step is usually the production by resonance of chemical hormones which have absorbed certain frequency patterns in the living wave system and retained them in their molecular structure.   Transplanta-

[1] This distinction between living and non-living entities may seem arbitrary but it is of fundamental significance.   Living entities are characterized by their integral properties and since their properties are inherent in the sources the latter must themselves have integral properties.   Such sources can normally only come into existence by a process of splitting and duplication of similar sources.

tion experiments show that these chemical hormones, as well as similar chemical substances made from inorganic material, can themselves activate certain parts of a living wave system.[1] Oxygen together with water in liquid form can be regarded as forming a "hormone" of a very general type, capable of initiating the activities of most genes and genii. It is interesting to note the analogy between hormones and radiation. They are both non-living carriers of energy and special frequencies, they both cause activation and expansion, but the first serve as a link between living wave systems and the latter between non-living wave systems.

The general genie organizes the activities of the subordinate genii. It determines which parts of the growing gastrula or the changing larva shall become a head or a heart, a leg or a wing. In the embryo it has a definite location, and its signals to the subordinate genii can be thought of as travelling chiefly along definite structural channels in the expanding genie, and *the channels often become observable as nerve fibers.* The general genie determines the general plan of the animal, the subordinate genii determine the structure and functioning of the organs. If there is no interference with their work, all the parts

---

[1] This explains the fact that the activating substances are not destroyed by boiling. The chemical hormones produced by the endocrine glands are substances of the type here mentioned. The vitamins are chemical hormones produced in nature by resonance in foreign animals or plants.

finally work together in the most wonderful harmony.

At this point the critical reader may well object and say that I am no longer speaking of physics, but of something beyond physics, of supernatural or spiritualistic conceptions, which may only exist in my own imagination. The physical aspect of a genie [1] is certainly far beyond the field of present-day physics. It is, nevertheless, a structure with space and time properties, and it belongs thus to the domain of physics, which deals with nothing else than material and immaterial space-time structures. In the writer's opinion we must include the genii in the class of physical entities; they belong to the class of immaterial structures of which several kinds are already known to the science of physics. We all admit the existence of the materialized forms of these entities, as living organized structures of more or less differentiated cells, and to explain the existence of highly organized structures we must either assume an action of supernatural agencies or of organizers like genii. The writer believes that there are no supernatural agencies whatever; things and phenomena inevitably appear supernatural when man does

[1] The concept of a genie as used in the following can to some extent be regarded as a modern scientific version of Aristotle's *entelechis*. A similar concept has been reintroduced in modern science by the eminent biologist Hans Driesch. (Gifford Lectures, 1907 and 1908.)

not understand them, and natural when he has become a little more familiar with them.

There are certain reasons for the assumption that at least some of the more important genii, when in their potential form in the eggcells, probably reside in the cytoplasm rather than in the nucleus. The cytoplasm is a *fluid* body, nevertheless it has a very complicated structure. This structure can not be made visible by staining but its existence can be shown by the fact that the movements within the cytoplasm take place along definite channels. It can also be shown by centrifuging, in which process jerky movements of the suspended bodies are observed in the fluid. The existence of highly complicated structures in a fluid body like the cytoplasm of an eggcell is in itself a very strong argument for the existence of immaterial organizers as the underlying cause of the fluid structure. These entities must be able to resist the tendency of the heat motion in the fluid to destroy the structure. All the hereditary factors of an animal, including those which determine its consciousness and mental characteristics, must exist in potential form in the fertilized eggcell. To the writer it seems inconceivable that any atomic configuration, however complex, can *by itself* represent all the hereditary properties and faculties.

A plant or an animal has a marvelous structure in space and time. The most remarkable thing is the general cooperation between its parts and the special cooperation between adjacent cells, which makes certain tissues function as organs with special functions.

As a simple example we shall take the heart of some animal. All the cells in the heart have the same chromosomes and also the same genes as the other cells in the body of this particular animal. We have assumed that the general genie originally had activated special genes in a certain cell group or tissue and thus had determined which part of the animal embryo was to become a heart. The resultant physical development and cooperation between the different parts of the heart can be visualized in two somewhat different ways. For the sake of brevity we shall in the following denote the immaterial space-time structures in the genes by the term *gene-spirits*. In the developing embryo the gene-spirits of the heart genes may be visualized as being able to cooperate, because their complex electric fields are "tuned" in the unison necessary to secure proper development of and cooperation within the organ. Or else one of the heart genes has the special power of bringing the spirits of the heart genes into cooperation. It may develop the whole organ, or electric impulses may travel along definite channels to all its parts. If a special "gene" carries this power of organization, it would be consistent with our former terminology to designate its spirit by the name genie, or specifically by the term *heart genie*, and regard it as centered in a particular cell or cell group in the heart.

There are several reasons for the belief that the genii are in some ways similar to gene spirits, that they are, at least in some cases, centered in certain localities, and that their activity is often directed along definite channels. In a fully developed heart a certain nodel tissue, similar to nerve tissue, is the pacemaker and the beat originates in a modified group of nerve cells, similar to the *neurones* and *ganglia* (nerve centers) in the brain and in the spinal cord. The neurones in the body of an animal were formerly considered quiescent systems ready to react to external excitation. Such systems are now known to be *dynamic*, that is, they have both space and time properties and they also have a certain degree of *automatic activity*, indicating that they contain the particular kind of space-time structure which we have called genii.

In an inorganic substance like a molecule or a crystal all the sources (neutrons, electrons, positrons) are *material* and *non-living*, that is, they have finite and definite rest masses and do not reproduce themselves by splitting. The structural properties of the associated wave systems (matter waves) in inorganic substances are hence completely defined by the atomic configurations and by the external field. In a living substance, on the other hand, there are in addition *living*, *immaterial* sources, and their wave systems,

when activated and developed by hormones, interfere with the matter waves and tend to bring the two
wave systems into coincidence and resonance.   A
living wave system is sustained by a single source or
a coordinated system of sources and can yield very
little, but the non-living wave system of a fluid with
many independent sources and a great variety of
actual and potential frequencies can easily be modified.   A permanent and effective association between
inorganic matter and living sources can hence be expected only for fluids with unstable structure of certain composition (e.g. proteins, protoplasm).   We
can then understand why the structure of a gastrula
or a neurone is almost entirely due to the properties
of the activated living sources and that the same kind
of molecules can serve as building material for many
kinds of living tissues.   We must not, however, overlook the possibility of the existence of *non-living*,
immaterial sources (other than photons), that is,
massless sources which do not *directly* originate from
a process of splitting and have less marked integral
properties than the living sources. Cellulose and non-
living proteins seem to contain sources of this type.

We can now understand the relationship between
the processes in neurones, nerve fibers and muscles.
The nerve fibers extend from the neurones to the fibers in the muscles and must be regarded as integral
parts of the neurones themselves.   The expansion of
the living wave system in the neurones which occurs

at activation by a hormone is observed as an impulse or a "wave" in the nerve fibers, usually described in terms of rapid chemical and electric changes. When the waves reach the muscle with which the nerve fibers are connected, the immaterial structure in the muscle is also modified, and the muscle fibers tend to contract or change their shape.[1] If there is no opposition, little energy is needed for this process. If, however, the contraction is opposed by external conditions, e.g. by gravitational forces or by fluid pressure, large amounts of energy may be needed for the structural changes. Certain electric bonds are then broken and other bonds are formed. In this process certain carbohydrates are split into molecules of lactic acid, and energy is quickly set free during this decomposition. As in atoms this means either that the non-living wave system of the molecular structure itself changes, or that the particles can move from cells of low energy to cells of higher energy. Whichever picture we prefer we can understand that the atoms can now follow the changing structure of the wave system in the muscle fibers without violating the law of conservation of energy. If sufficient "fuel" in the muscle is not available, the muscle may

[1] It is interesting to note that this simple and temporary change in shape is here assumed to be accomplished by the same kind of mechanism which causes the more complex and permanent changes involved in embryonic development and metamorphosis. The muscular changes are of the reversible type, however.

not respond at all or only in an incomplete manner. A difference between the non-living wave system in the muscle (the matter waves) and the living wave system sustained by the nerve fibers (which must be regarded as living sources in the muscle since they are extensions from the living sources in the neurones) then develops; in fact, the muscle is in the same state of tension as is a growing embryo the natural development of which is prevented by lack of energy sufficient to overcome mechanical obstacles. If the load is much too great for the available energy, the latter can do little or no *mechanical* work. In this case the energy is "wasted" and appears as *heat*, that is, as internal agitation in the atomic structure. The products of the chemical changes are removed from the muscle by the blood stream, and new fuel is stored in the muscle when it again is relaxed.

In certain parts of a living body it is the structural rather than the functional organization which is the more striking. As a relatively simple case consider the factors which determine the structure of the external ears in men. The shape of the ears varies from one individual to another; in fact, ears are as individual as finger prints. The building material consists of cells, which all have the same potential capabilities as other cells in the body. Let us try to compare this cellular structure with that of a crystal composed of certain atomic nuclei and electrons. When a crystal grows in a solution, the immaterial space-time structure, which gives the molecules their structural characteristics, captures ions with similar immaterial structures. The structure is then repeated over and over again, and the crystal can be regarded as a giant molecule. By analogy we may try to picture the two ears as two similar "magnifications" of certain cells, the structure of which is determined by the "spirits of the ear-genes." The latter are activated by hormones, directed to their proper locations by a genie, which is probably centered in some nerve tissue. This genie also activates other genes in neighboring regions, thus securing a complete organ of hearing.

Organic structures are much more complex than crystals, and it is in most cases impossible to introduce sharp delimitations for the activities of gene groups or genii. We are again forced to the conception of an *expansion* of an immaterial structure. As the general genie expands and causes the first organization of the embryo, so the subordinate genii seem to expand and extend the field of their structure-defining influence. If we retain the analogy with crystal formation, we may say that an immaterial, living structure (a genie) expands within a mixture of identical but very complex bodies (cells with chromosomes), the space-time structure of the genie determining which of the component molecules (gene groups) shall crystallize in one region of the embryo or organ and which in another. The genii act in many cases with the aid of non-living structures (growth producing hormones) which cause "crystallization" of the proper genes. The "crystallization of a gene" means that a particular gene or gene group expands, imparting its structure and properties to the whole cell (differentiation), other genes being not activated and hence undeveloped. The action of the gastrula genie on the morula, the general genie on the animal as a whole, the subordinate genii on the organs, and the gene spirits on the cells, are probably all of the same nature.

The conception of nerves as being channels fixed at an early stage of development is supported by certain facts about their growth. Nerve fibers are first formed as protrusions from nerve cells; the protrusions grow in length, not by a process of cell division, but by a process of *cell extension*. The nerve fibers are hence integral parts of the neurones themselves. Neurones are originally formed during embryonic development and during metamorphosis, and damaged ones can never be re-formed. It seems to the writer that the nervous system in an animal is the physical aspect of a system of genii in its fully developed form, and that the expansion of this system in the dorsal mesoderm of the gastrula or in the changing larva is directly observable as a growth of nerve tissue and a formation of interconnected neurones. The peculiar way in which nerve tissue grows indicates that it really arises from an expansion of an immaterial structure in the *cytoplasm* of certain cells.

We realize now the existence of a new fundamental distinction between a non-living body, like a crystal, and a living body, like a neurone. A crystal is formed by *accretion* and can be dissolved into its elementary parts, the molecules. A neurone is formed by *expansion* and can not be subdivided without losing its essential properties. A crystal is fundamentally a *composite* body; a neurone is fundamentally an *elementary* body, in other words, an integral unit.

It is interesting to note that nerve impulses in general can be detected *outside* the neurones and the nerve fibers. It seems that the activation of neurones is *always* accompanied by an expansion of the living wave system beyond its visual boundaries. We can then understand how the organizing effect of genii, which in the higher animals is associated with a growth of nerve tissue, can extend far beyond the visual boundaries of the nerve cells, and we can visualize how *concerted* nerve impulses originate by expansion of the living wave system in the neurones. (Cf. p. 178 f.)

We have in the higher organisms a "hierarchy" of organizers or genii, beginning with the general genie of the animal, continuing with the genii of the organs, and ending with the genes in the individual cells. The specific gene spirits are the responsive material on which the genii finally act, and the action is transmitted by "messengers" (hormones) in the form of chemical substances or electric states travelling with the blood or along the nerves.

The development of displaced eye lenses in an embryo, as mentioned before, and the results of transplantations in different stages of embryonic development, can be understood if we assume that the general genii expands first, then the subordinate genii, and finally the gene spirits.   In animals undergoing metamorphosis the egg cells must contain an additional system of genii which expands in the process.   In some cases subordinate genii expand during a later period in the life cycle.   The development of the flower in a plant, for instance, can be regarded as the physical manifestation of the expansion of a "flower genie."

Many biologists regard the organizing entity as some sort of a "chemical substance," which acts as a "morphogenetic hormone," and they use the term *organizers* for this class of hormones.   But a morphogenetic hormone, if it existed, must in general have nearly all the properties of the complete animal; it must in some form represent the heart and the liver, the eyes and the ears, and to call such a substance "chemical" does not at all convey the correct idea of its essential properties.   The system of genes and genii is the morphogenetic entity, but it consists of many parts any one of which can become effective.

A particular subordinate genie can expand and form an organ, and a particular gene spirit can expand and form a particular kind of cell.

A remarkable case of the activities of genii is found among certain species of the pelagic floating *Siphonophora*, of which the best known example is the Portuguese Man-of-war. These animals live in tropical waters and are related to the common jellyfish. They occur either as free swimming individuals (medusae) or in the form of organized colonies. The individuals are born by a budding process from the composite animal and can also reproduce themselves. It has been observed that sometimes a group of individuals cling together and gradually change into an *organized* colony, which hence is formed by accretion and transformation of *well developed animals* and not by cell division or by transformation of undifferentiated cells. Parts of the colony become the connective or the floating elements, others become the prehensile, digestive or reproductive organs. If the organized animal is broken up the parts do not die, but lose their special structure and functions and become again free-swimming individuals.

One type of organization can seemingly be replaced by another, as in metamorphosis, but the change apparently is in some cases reversible. It seems quite possible that a simple chemical hormone could be found which applied to a particular individual in a group of Siphonophora could start the expansion of the wave of organization from any assigned place and thus transform the group into an organized colony. The presence or absence of certain simple chemicals would probably have the same effect as a mechanical breakup and would cause the transformation of an organized colony into a group of medusae. Perhaps a hormone could also be found which could, for example, change a prehensile organ into a digestive, and another which would work in the opposite direction. A hormone may cause the expansion of one particular genie and the contraction of another which has already expanded, and also prevent the expansion of all the rest of the subordinate genii.[1] Similar phenomena occur among the genes and manifest themselves as differentiation, dedifferentiation, and redifferentiation of the cells.

All space-time structures obey certain conservation laws. In physics we speak about a conservation of mass and energy, of linear and angular momentum, and of electric charge. We have also a non-variability of elementary properties, like the charge and rest mass of an electron and a proton, and the value of the quantum of action. In the organic world we have a

---

[1] This theory is supported by the fact that hormones can be either "positive" or "negative," and their efficiency can be graded, that is, they can be more or less effective and more or less inhibitory. A positive hormone transmits energy to, and a negative hormone absorbs energy from, a living wave system. The hormones have no effect on the sources of the living wave systems. The sources themselves seem to have no definite space extension and appear to be indestructible. Cf. p. 151 ff.

retention of certain structural properties in gene spirits and genii, in spite of their splitting and expansion. It is this conservation of structural properties which is responsible for the similarity between parents and offspring. This principle of conservation applies also to mental phenomena, it is responsible for the stability of the mental characteristics of a race and even for the memory of an individual, as will be explained in another connection.

The reason why genii appear so mysterious and strange can be traced, I think, to the fact that their expansion and their peculiar means of communication sometimes make their field of influence very extensive. If this field were about a million (10^6) times smaller, they would appear to have about the same size as before their expansion, and if they were 10^{25} times larger they would perhaps be as large as the whole universe,[1] where light is a "hormone" travelling along structural paths in space-time (geodesics) and activating the "spirits of the atoms." In neither

[1] We may well regard the metrical space-time field of the universe as a "super genie," guiding the motions of photons (light beams), atoms and stars along definite paths in space-time. This gives us a good picture of the subtle nature of genii and their relationship to matter. If we interpret the red shift in the spectra of the extragalactic nebulae as actual recession, this super genie has been expanding for more than two thousand million years and the expansion is still going on. In this case the genie defines motion rather than space-structure, because the cosmic space and time scales are quite different from those in atoms and genes, in which we can not study the motions of the material elements.

case would we regard the genii as more mysterious than other space-time structures.

Before continuing the discussion of genes and genii and their properties, it becomes necessary to take up the questions of heredity and of the origin and evolution of life on earth.

CHAPTER 7

Heredity and Genes

I<small>N THE</small> middle of the last century there lived in
Moravia an Augustine monk named Gregor
Mendel, who became abbot of a monastery in Brünn.
He loved the flowers in his garden, he studied their
fertilization and was interested in the hybrids which
he could produce. He crossed varieties and species
of plants and studied carefully the consequences.
His conclusions were published in 1865 in an obscure
scientific journal and to his surprise attracted practically no attention. He died in 1884 at the age of 60.
His personality and work were soon forgotten—he
had disappeared like so many others of the human
race.

But biological science did not stand still; the urge
of obtaining new knowledge, so characteristic of
human beings, was forcing men everywhere to study
the origin and development of plants and animals.
One important problem that called for investigation
was that of the transfer of physical and mental characteristics from parents to their offspring. De Vries,
Tschermak, and Correns, working independently in
the last years of the 19th century, had found sur-

prising rules concerning heredity in plants and animals. They found in 1900 that Mendel had published in 1865 the fundamental laws governing heredity.

What are then these laws? They can be most easily understood by giving a few examples. Mendel studied varieties of the common edible garden peas, but we shall here describe a somewhat simpler case, the Japanese plant *Mirabilis jalapa,* the common "four-o'clocks." This plant occurs in three varieties, one with red, another with white, and a third with pink flowers. Except for color the plants are very much alike. As in so many other common flowering plants the female organs of reproduction consist of a group of ovules and a pistil with a stigma. The male organs consist of stamens carrying the pollen, and this is ordinarily carried by insects from one plant to another. When the pollen become attached to the stigma, sperm cells from the pollen travel down the pistil and reach the ovules, which then start their development.

If seeds from the plants with red flowers are cultivated, the new plants will all have red flowers. From their seeds in turn new generations of plants with red flowers may be obtained, and we have a so-called "pure" line of red flowering peas. The plants are "breeding true," as the saying is.

If we do the same thing with plants having white

flowers, the same rule holds. They also are breeding true.

If we transfer pollen from red flowers to white flowers the next generation will all have pink flowers. The same occurs, if we transfer pollen from white flowers to the red ones. If we self pollinate the pink flowering plants, the next generation will consist of red flowers, white flowers and pink flowers in the proportion, one to one to two.

If we cross the white flowers with pink flowers, the first generation shows a mixture of white and pink flowers in about equal proportion, but no red. If we cross the red flower with pink flowers the first generation is a mixture of red with pink flowers, also in equal proportion, but no white flowers appear.

In most cases the result of cross breeding appears to be more complicated than the above example. One character seems to dominate another, and the latter does not become evident, if the first character exists in the plant or animal. The first character is called *dominant*, the second is called *recessive*.

Mendel observed several such cases. He crossed a plant having yellow peas with another having green peas. The first generation had all yellow seeds. When he cultivated this generation, protected from outside pollination, the new plants had yellow or green seeds in the proportion three to one. The "yellow" was a dominant character, the "green" a recessive. The colors did not blend as in the flowers we have just described, but one character suppressed the other.

Sometimes characters are unhealthy and even lethal. In most observed cases they are recessive, for, if they were dominant and effective, the offspring in the wild state of the particular animal or plant would be handicapped and might even succumb to disease or die out completely, in which case biologists would have difficulty in finding specimens for their studies.

In most cases we are dealing with mixed characters. If a pea which is yellow and round is crossed with one that is green and wrinkled, the peas in the first generation are all yellow and round. By inbreeding, we get a second generation with yellow-round, green-round, yellow-wrinkled and green-wrinkled seeds in the proportion 9:3:3:1. In this case roundness is dominant to wrinkledness, and yellow prevails over green. It appears that we have four different and independent characters: yellowness, greenness, roundness and wrinkledness. Although we simply mix them in a haphazard way, the result can be predicted with the same accuracy as when we compute the probabilities of combinations.

Similar rules governing the occurrence of all kinds of characteristics have been found. The list contains a variety of characters, like special forms of leaves, susceptibility and immunity to rust and certain sicknesses, the shape and coloration of insects, color of eyes, the plumage of fowls, the horns of cattle, and according to several authorities also mental defects and unusual capabilities.

It is obvious that we are dealing with some fundamental law governing inheritance. Some units are transmitted independently of others, other units are transmitted in groups to the offspring. Some characters, if they are present at all, have a dominating effect, they suppress or hide the recessive characters, and the latter appear again if the dominant character happens to be absent in an individual of a subsequent generation. A mixing or shuffling of elementary hereditary units seems to occur.

Before we describe the mechanism of inheritance we must try to answer the important question, "Are all characters and faculties inherited, or do any physical or mental characters exist which are not inherited?"

A plant or an animal is a product of its inherent nature and its environment. If the environment is entirely unsuitable the organism simply does not develop at all, however perfect its inherited constitution may be. If the conditions are better the organism may grow and develop in a stunted and imperfect fashion. Only a few seeds or eggs will develop, those that have inherited hardiness, immunity to disease, and potential means of protection from enemies. In the best environmental conditions the race will in general be extremely prolific.

In order to understand more easily the difference between heredity and non-hereditary characters, we shall give the classical example of bean cultures, scientifically studied and analyzed by the Danish botanist Johannsen.

He started with a number of beans, all from the same plant, and cultivated them. The fact that the beans multiply by self-fertilization made it easy to protect the plants from foreign pollen. In the first generation he graded the beans according to their weight and planted them in separate groups, each with a small range in weight. The beans in the second generation were also graded according to weight, the idea being to find out if by repeated selection of heavy beans a strain with uniformly heavy beans could be developed. The result was that any individual plant carried beans of different weight, but the selection of heavy beans had no effect on the subsequent generations. Evidently the weight was due to many causes, like position in the pod, the amount of sunshine on different pods, and so on, but the weight was, in this case at least, not a hereditary property.

Next he studied beans as commercially sold, graded the collection according to weight and performed the same experiment. Now the result was quite different. The heavy beans when planted gave for generation after generation heavy beans, and the lighter beans produced lighter ones. But it was impossible to go beyond a certain limit by the selection of heavy beans, for the increase in size stopped and could not be carried further. He was able to purify the strains in his original collection to some extent, however. In one case he found no less than five true breeding strains, each of them no longer capable of modification by selection, even if carried out for many generations.

This experiment teaches us that weight is not necessarily a hereditary character. There are separate strains with beans of different average weight, and the strains are so much alike that it is impossible to distinguish them from one another. Each has both heavy and light beans, and it is not possible by simply weighing or examining to tell to which strain a particular bean or plant belongs.

Everybody knows that certain characters are not inherited. A broken bone, a birthmark, or an accidentally lost finger, is not inherited. The ability to play the violin is not inherited, but the aptitude for learning to do it is inherited and varies greatly among individuals. According to Mendel's rules we should expect the probability of becoming a great musician to be greatly increased in case both the father and the mother have musical talent. It may even be that in some cases musical ability is "recessive." A man or a woman may have it without conscious knowledge of the fact. It may be dominated or rather suppressed by other characters incompatible with musical talent, as, for instance, an organic defect in the ears.

Detailed memories are, so far as the writer's knowledge goes, never inherited. Special memory elements and groups of such elements may well be inherited, in most cases in sub-conscious form. These are the instincts in animals.

Another inherited character group is called *xenophobia*,[1] the hatred of strangers. Animals of common ancestry found out in their subconscious mind that it was practical to live in closed societies. They could then help one another and fight their enemies more effectively. A group which had this instinct survived in the struggle for life. Other races which did not have this instinct disappeared from the earth, apparently without leaving a trace. Wild dogs hated wild cats, and vice versa. They fought for the same kind of food. The hatred has—I am ashamed to admit it—survived to the present time. The hormones which activate this gene system seem to be secreted with great facility and abundance at the present time among members of the human race. Nations are arrayed against nations, one race against another, white people against black people, white

---

[1] It may be of interest to note that the old Greeks used the word *barbaros* (a barbaric foreigner) and they also used the word *xenos* (a stranger and a guest).

against yellow, the adherents of one economic, political or religious system against those of another. We cannot get rid of the gene complex in our bodies, but we can regulate the secretion of the activating hormones. A mixing of races and nationalities and a suppression of race consciousness has been proved to be helpful in this respect.

Some animals, like ants, termites and bees, have inherited a social order with strict distribution of work. It has probably developed gradually; one little element at a time has been added to the rest, provided it served the good purpose of assisting in the acquisition of food or of protecting the group from enemies. In the case of termites Eugène Marais has made the important suggestion that the whole termitary represents a single "animal," similar to the organized colony of Siphonophora. If this is the case the workers and the soldiers represent special "organs," the general genie is centered in the body of the queen, which is the "brain center" of the community, and the coordinating "nerve impulses" follow the enclosed channels in the termitary. The fact seems to be well established that some kind of communication exists between the termites and the queen because the highly organized activities are almost impossible to explain in any other way. When the queen is killed all organized activities immediately cease.

Leaving for the present these phenomena, we shall now take up the physical processes and mechanism of heredity.   How are hereditary characters transmitted from one living organism to another, and what is the nature of the transmitted elements?

It has been known for some time that the only elements, which can be responsible for the transfer of hereditary characters, are the germ cells or gametes.   In asexual reproduction, like ordinary cell division and in parthenogenetic reproduction, there is a single parent cell, while in sexual reproduction there are two slightly different kinds of gametes which must carry the hereditary potentialities.   Since the chromosomes are known to be distributed in such a way that equal parts are transferred from both parents, there can be no doubt that the chromosomes are carriers of hereditary elements.

The chromosomes are in general very small things. A few are about a hundredth part of an inch in length, many are much smaller, and in some cases they can attain gigantic size.   It is obvious that the number of hereditary elements which determine the physical body structure and the subconscious mental heritage of an animal must be enormously large.   It was thus natural for investigators to study the internal structure of the chromosomes to see if it was possible to locate special hereditary characters in the chromosomes themselves.   We must admire the ingenuity, patience and perseverance of the students of *genetics*, as the science of heredity and genes is called, when we read about the marvelous work in this field.   Only a few typical examples with an outline of general results can here be given.

The chromosomes are now regarded as built of a great number of *genes*, each carrying elementary hereditary elements. The physical effects of genes are more easily studied than the mental. We can, for instance, study the body color, shape of wings, color of eyes among insects, but we can not study the corresponding modifications of their sensations and feelings.

There are many cases similar to that of the plant with red and white flowers. The phenomenon is easy to interpret. There are genes carrying the "white" and the "red" characteristic. A plant with white flowers has only "white" genes, a red flowering plant has only the "red" gene in its chromosome structure. We have said that in body cells the chromosomes occur in pairs (homologous mates); in every cell of the white flowering plant there is a "white" gene in both of the homologous mates, and in the red-flowering plant there is a "red" gene in both the corresponding mates. When the germ cells are formed, there is a reduction in the chromosomes to half their normal number. The gametes are formed in the flowers, some of the gametes containing one of the homologous mates, others the other mate. In a flower the ovules and the pollen carry only one of the particular chromosomes; in the white flowers both kinds of cells carry the white genes, in the red flowers they both carry the red genes.   When the plants are crossed by transfer of pollen from a white flower to a red flower, or vice versa, we can only get combinations of white genes with red genes, and the first generation has thus only pink flowers.   By interbreeding these plants we can get combinations of white genes with white genes, white with red, red with white and red with red.   The fertilized egg cells in the ovules develop into seeds which produce plants with genes carrying the white-white, white-red, red-white or red-red potentialities in all the body cells of the plants.   When the special hormones carried by the sap in the plant come to the developing flowers they change the color potentialities into actualities, and we have thus a new generation consisting of one quarter red-flowering plants, one quarter white-flowering plants and one half pink-flowering plants.

A chemical hormone can be regarded as a non-living frequency pattern stabilized by a corresponding atomic structure.   When detached from its living origin a hormone retains some of the frequency pattern inherent in this origin and can activate certain genes and cause the development of their wave systems. The complex color combination in many flowers is the effect of chemical substances carried by the sap and interacting with and modified by the living wave systems in the flower.   A gene is often characterized by the *absence* of certain qualities which it normally possesses, e.g. the power of producing a red pigment.

In the case of the flowers just mentioned the color-producing genes were located one in each of a pair of homologous mates. In many cases a group of characters are transmitted as a whole. This is regarded as due to the fact that the corresponding genes lie in the same chromosome and can hence be transferred as groups in fertilization and in cell division. These are called *linked characters*. The reader may ask how it is possible to tell that such groups do not belong to the same gene, or that there may not be complicated genes, carrying a very great number of observable characters. The elementary character of the genes has been established by the existence of what are called *mutations*, the nature of which will be fully discussed in the next chapter.

As an example we might mention the experiments with species of the fruit fly (Drosophila). The wild fly has in general a gray body color and long wings. By breeding in a laboratory a black variety has been developed with long wings, another with very small, vestigial wings, a third of the gray variety with vestigial wings, while the fourth is the wild type with gray body and long wings. In most cases the black body color and vestigial wings are transmitted together in crossing, and so are the gray body color and the long wings, but the existence of the other combinations shows that the double character is not due to the same gene.

In some cases the linking of characters is changed and remains changed for several generations. This is an important fact, which has thrown much light on the nature of the chromosomes and the genes. It shows that the homologous chromosomes, during their twisting around one another like two snakes, can become crossed and two pieces can be exchanged when the chromosomes finally part, and we get then a new linkage of hereditary factors. Such twistings and crossings occur during the *conjugation* of chromosomes in the production of gametes. As a result we may get gray body color combined with vestigial wings, and black color combined with long wings.

Often characters are linked with the sex. It can be shown that the genes are in this case carried by the X-chromosomes, of which in the mammals the males carry one and the females two. A male can therefore carry only one type of a particular gene in the X-chromosomes in his body, which gene may be normal or modified, while a female can carry one normal and one diseased gene, one in each of the X-chromosomes.

For instance, *color blindness* (the inability to distinguish between red and green) is in general regarded as due to a defect in the gene system carried by the X-chromosomes. A man has only one

X-chromosome, and he is thus either color blind or not. A woman has two X-chromosomes, one or perhaps both of which may be affected. If both are affected she is color blind, but if only one of them is affected, she is not color blind, for she needs only one of these genes to secure proper perception of color. In the latter case her male children with a "normal" man may be color blind or not, for none of them has inherited any X-chromosome from his father, they have all inherited them from their mother. The female children can not be color blind, for they have all inherited an X-chromosome and hence a normal gene from their father, if not from their mother. They can, however, carry the disease in a latent form.

We said before that hereditary elements are also carried by the cytoplasm as well as in the nucleus, and whether we call them genes or genii or anything else is a matter of definition. There are several reasons for this statement. The small bodies in the cytoplasm, which are called plastids, also carry hereditary characters. The plastids are self-perpetuating and in their behavior are somewhat similar to micro-organisms. The "chloroplastids" in plant cells are responsible for the production of the green chlorophyll in most plants and themselves contain chlorophyll. Certain chloroplastids do not contain chlorophyll, and a seed with such an abnormal chloroplastid develops into a white plant without chloro-

phyll.   Since sperms and pollen contain little or no
cytoplasm, it is clear that any hereditary factors which
are carried by the cytoplasm can only be transmitted
by female germ cells, in other words, the corresponding characters are transmitted by *maternal* inheritance
only.

It has been found that a sperm can cause development of a fraction of an egg cell which contains no
nucleus.   In this case the genes come from the father,
and only those maternal characters can be transmitted
which are carried by the cytoplasm in the egg cell.
By such experiment it has been found that the early
development of the embryo is probably entirely determined by *maternal* heritage and hence by the
properties of the cytoplasm and not by the genes in
the chromosomes.

Most of our knowledge of the distribution of
genes in the chromosomes has been acquired during
the last twenty years.   Particularly prominent in
this search have been Thomas Hunt Morgan and his
co-workers.   They have succeeded in mapping the
position of many hundreds of genes in the chromosomes of the banana fly (*Drosophila melanogaster*).
The mapping was made possible by a study of the
degree of linkages among genes and of the probabilities of "crossing-overs," that is, the interchange of
gene groups.   The size of the genes could be esti-
mated, they are far beyond direct vision in the microscopes of the highest power.   When we think about

the marvelous diversity and number of separate characters carried, for instance, by the extremely small
sperm cell, just visible in an ordinary microscope, our
thoughts wander off in admiration for the Creator
and Organizer of the universe.

Genes are not small in themselves, they are ordinarily about ten or a hundred times larger than
ordinary atoms. They are only small relative to our
bodies and to the light waves for which our eyes are
sensitive. A little gene may, for all we know, be a
little miniature universe in itself. We shall see that
there are some reasons to believe that this statement
is more than a mere metaphor.

CHAPTER 8

The Origin and Development
of Life on Earth

THERE IS hardly a human being who has not occasionally asked the question: "What is the origin of men, animals and plants?" The answer is that they come from eggs. Where do the respective eggs come from? From the respective animals and plants. A hen comes from an egg and an egg from a hen. The chain seems to run on and on; its beginning seems to be lost in the darkness of time, and there is no other end than the complete extinction of the race.

The most simple observations tell us that many different animals show a number of similar features. A large group of animals have heads with two eyes and two ears, a mouth and a nose. They have often four legs with jointed members, but their hands, and feet, paws or hoofs differ in many respects. Then we have the birds with their remarkable ability to fly, the fishes and the reptiles, each group consisting of members with many similarities. Then we have the insects, the molluscs, the starfishes, the worms, and all the strange animals in the waters, and we have the invisible germs and bacteria. In the vegetable kingdom we have all kinds of plants and trees, algae and mosses, down to simple spores, which seem to have a life of their own. These animals and plants, in spite of their great difference in appearance and mode of living, are structures consisting of cells with chromosomes and genes, although the very lowest forms may have a simpler structure.

Animals and plants can be classified into groups, and these appear to be linked together in a chain system with many branches. In many cases there are fairly large gaps or missing links in the chains. I have not here particularly in mind "the missing link" between certain antropoid apes and men, for this gap, *so far as physical characteristics are concerned,* is much smaller than other gaps in the system of organisms living on the earth at the present time.

If we study the recorded history of animals and plants on earth we find that certain species of animals have disappeared, and this has happened even within the last hundred years. Certain animals like the American buffalo have rapidly decreased in numbers and might have become completely extinct had it not been for special protection. In this case the decimation has been due partly to the disappearance of vast pastures and partly to man's greed. Even certain races of men would have nearly disappeared,

had they not been protected. Such is the case with
the natives of what we now call the Hawaiian Islands, that beautiful place in the Pacific Ocean.
When discovered by white people, the native popula-
tion was much larger than at present and consisted
of healthy, intelligent people, who had reached a
relatively high moral level. White men carried the
germs of diseases, particularly tuberculosis and pneu-
monia, to the islands, and the natives had never had
occasion to develop the necessary protection.[1] Certain species of animals, when suddenly brought into
contact with other new, but not necessarily hostile
species, have utterly vanished from the earth. Similar phenomena occur also with insects, plants and
trees, although the cause is often large-sized para-
sites instead of microscopic germs.

We may go far back in time by studying the
traces left of animals and plants in the different
geological strata of the earth. If such strata are not
disturbed, they are made up of horizontal layers
often formed by deposits on the bottom of oceans or
large lakes. There we may find fossilized bones,
shells or parts of animals, imprints of animals and
plants, and carbonized trees, which latter give us

[1] Chemical substances (antitoxins) are produced by the dead
germs of a disease and tend to stop its further progress. Part of
the antitoxin remains in the body and is ready to exercise its
protection in case of a new attack of the disease. Antitoxin
(serum) can be transferred by injections to animals and men,
thus causing immunity to particular diseases (e.g. vaccination).

the coal we use today.   In some cases bones of many
animals are mixed together in a special locality.   Undoubtedly animals which came to drink at a water
hole were trapped in the soft and swampy earth and
so perished.   A tar pit covered with water made a
most effective trap, as in the case of La Brea pits in
Southern California, where bones from animals have
accumulated for some 100,000 years or more.

When geological strata are undisturbed there can
be no doubt that the lower strata have been formed
earlier than the upper ones.   We may even use the
radioactive disintegration products to determine the
ages of the different layers, thereby actually reading
the "clock" nature itself has placed in the rocks.
Examination of the remains of organic life in the
geological strata has revealed the remarkable fact
that life has changed considerably during the last
thousand million years.   There are no traces of any
life in the rocks older than about 600 or 700 million
years.   The oldest well preserved fossils are the
trilobites, belemnites, and ammonites, which are related to the cuttlefish, octopus, and nautilus of the
present day.   These fossils may be seen in nearly any
slab of limestone, and, since they were forms of
marine life, their general occurrence is evidence that
at this period practically the whole earth was covered
with water.

The first vertebrates appeared about 400 million
years ago, as forerunners of the fishes and of the

amphibia. The occurrence of the latter indicates that by this time land had begun to appear, probably as extended swamps. At about the same time insects made their first appearance, plants began to appear and later trees. Then came the first reptiles some 200 or 300 million years ago, and they seem to have developed into the big monsters now reconstructed in our museums. The first forerunners of the mammals seem to occur about 150 million years ago. There also appeared some strange birds, which looked like flying reptiles, but had feathers (Archaeopteryx). Plants with flowers made their appearance, also placental mammals—in which the embryo is nourished from a separate organ called *placenta*, which does not exist in the mammals indigenous to Australia. Then followed modern birds, and finally came men, that class of strange animals in which we are particularly interested since we all belong to it.

During this development or evolution the surface of the earth changed. At definite recurrent periods mountains were formed and rose from the seas, to be in turn eroded by water, leveled off, and partly deposited in the surrounding ocean. New mountains were formed, and some of them have lasted till the present time.

The earth's atmosphere gradually changed. Millions of years ago the sky was perpetually covered with clouds, through which no ray from the sun could penetrate deeply. The sky cleared slowly, a diffuse light appeared on earth, and finally the sun emerged in all its glory. The stars could now shine on the earth—their light giving messages to those who could interpret them, that the earth and the sun were not alone in the Universe.

The geological evidence for the gradual changes in life on the earth's surface is so strong that nobody who has studied it can deny its reality or its profound meaning. Many theories have been proposed to account for the remarkable phenomenon of this *evolution of life on earth*.

Since we know that "life begets life," and that the offspring is very similar to its parents, the first obvious explanation is that there is a change in the offspring, that the latter acquires in some way or other new properties or faculties. St. Hilaire developed the theory that if the change was unfavorable the individual died and disappeared, whereas, if the change was in a favorable direction with regard to the environmental conditions, the individuals lived and multiplied. There are some objections to this theory. One is that the monstrous forms, which sometimes appear in breeding and which St. Hilaire thought were of special importance in evolution, rarely if ever furnish individuals that have any advantage over their parents. In practically all cases they are unfit for life, at least in the wild state. Nevertheless, there are elements of truth in his theory as will later appear.

Bergson, in recent times, has suggested that life responds to environmental conditions in such a way that the offspring is often modified in a direction which we might well regard as favorable. It puts the cause of the change in a mystical property of life, the "élan vital," which conception does not explain the actual process or cause of development.

Lamarck started from the fact that the use of an organ improves it while disuse makes it less efficient. If the improvements could be inherited, an organ, like a bird's wings, could perhaps gradually be developed. But such qualities are in general not inherited. Further, if we waved our arms for a million generations, we could not develop wings with feathers; at the most we might develop strong arms. We may perhaps improve our vision by training, but even if such improvements were inherited, we could still not understand the development of an eye out of "nothing."

The theory has also been advanced that all the faculties of present-day life were inborn in the first life on earth. The favorable characters have been "unfolded," the unfavorable ones have been lost with the disappearance of unfit animals and plants.

Darwin, whose theories have been so widely discussed, regarded the chance [1] variations in plants and animals as the primary elements in evolution. These

---

[1] Darwin stated that the accidental nature of the variations may be only apparent.

variations may be helpful or harmful for the individual in the struggle for existence, and in the former case the variations, some of which he supposed to be hereditary, were actually incorporated in the race. *Natural selection* gradually improved the race, new forms of animal life came into existence, and the unfit forms disappeared from the earth.

Darwin was particularly looking for the cause of the variations, and we now turn to a search for this cause. Most variations are not inherited, but there are types of variations, which biologists call *mutations*, which are actually inherited.

First we will give a few typical examples. In 1791 a sheep farmer in Massachusetts found one day to his surprise that one of his ewes had born a male lamb with short, bowed legs. He thought that it would be to his advantage to have short-legged sheep that could not jump the fences he had erected. He crossed the strange sheep with normal sheep and found that the new character was inherited by the offspring, for some of them had short legs. He developed the new strain by breeding, and after a few generations it was breeding true. The new kind of sheep became very popular among the farmers up to the time of development of a better breed.

The Dutch botanist de Vries studied inheritance in plants and discovered facts that could be interpreted by Mendel's laws. In his search he came upon a field of Evening Primroses (*Oenothera La-*

marckiana), which appeared to have certain peculiarities. Many different variations occurred mixed together. The size, the leaves, and the flowers varied from one plant to another. He cultivated the new variations and found that many of them were breeding true.

In the Biological Laboratory of the Carnegie Institution of Washington new strains of water-fleas (Daphnia) have been developed and have been breeding true for many hundreds of generations. In the Kerchoff Biological Laboratory, where Morgan has made his studies during later years, new types of the fruit-fly have been developed, a few of which could probably survive in the wild state.

Evidently something may change in the chromosome complement or gene system of plants and animals, which, if transmitted to or occurring in the germ-cells, might well produce a new stable variety. Many experiments have been made to modify strains by changing the external conditions, but they have nearly all failed, so far as inherited properties go. We can change the color of a plant or an animal by proper illumination or heat treatment, but ordinarily we do not get any inherited characters in this way.

There are a few exceptions to this rule, however. The most striking is the fact that if we illuminate plants or seeds with x-rays, we obtain a great variety of plants, most of which have no survival qualities, however. There can be little doubt that new, perhaps stable varieties can be formed in this way. Recently it has been found that certain chemicals can also cause mutations.

Electrons, α-particles, x-rays and gamma rays act like very small energetic bullets, and we should expect their effect to be very powerful and highly localized. It is hence not surprising that radium and x-rays can produce effects on the chromosomes without permanently injuring the rest of the cell. It has been found that the chromosomes are often broken up, or clumped, or affected in other ways under such treatments. It is also not surprising that certain chemicals can produce similar effects, since recombination of atoms and molecules in chemical reactions is a common phenomenon. The unchanging nature of the chromosomes under ordinary conditions, in spite of the obviously great activity involved in splitting and conjugation (the latter in the reduction process), is so remarkable, that this fact alone points to the existence of an organizing structure of high stability and integrity.

Ordinary mutations are due to many causes. In a number of cases biologists have been able to study both the modifications in the chromosomes and the corresponding changes in the appearance of a plant or an animal. It has thus been found that mutations may be due to unequal splitting of the chromosomes, incomplete combination of chromosomes in conjugation, exchange of gene groups between homologous chromosomes (crossing-overs), transfer of gene groups from one chromosome to another, multiplication of chromosomes, disappearance of a particular part of a chromosome, and so on. Such changes in the gametes are duplicated in the body cells, provided the organism can function in spite of its modified gene system, and they are often repeated in the subsequent generations, in which case stable mutations are produced.

Mutations of the type in which whole or large parts of chromosomes are involved give rise to a simultaneous change of a great number of characters. The Evening Primrose, *Oenothera*, mentioned before, gives many examples of such mutations. But sometimes a single hereditary character has been modified, and in certain cases it has been possible to locate definitely the particular gene which has suffered the modification.

In nature radioactive materials produce gamma-rays, although the intensity of this radiation is in general very small. Ultraviolet light may cause somewhat similar effects, but the atmosphere lets through very little of this kind of radiation. *Cosmic radiation* is also largely absorbed by the atmosphere, but the secondary radiation it produces when striking the atoms in the atmosphere should be able to produce very violent and highly localized effect on the living cells. It may well be that changes in or losses of individual genes (*point mutations*) are often directly or indirectly caused by cosmic radiation.

We should expect that the mutations caused by modifications in the chromosomes and genes mentioned above are in general destructive or degrading. It should be remembered that only those mutations are retained in the race which do not prevent the germ cells from performing their normal functions and do not furnish too great a handicap to individuals in the struggle for existence. On the other hand, it is those changes which involve an advantage to the individual which would be retained in the wild state and would, if stable, give rise to new prolific species.

In many cases the changes must be regarded as due to modifications in the production of hormones rather than to a modification in the gene system. Since the genii are here assumed to regulate the production of hormones, we may say that the genii themselves are modified. An ordinary nose may in this way develop into the trunk of an elephant. A particular toe may become enlarged and others suppressed, and the hoof of a horse probably developed in some such way, because its ancestors lived in an environment where such a change would be advantageous.

Most animals show traces of *hermaphroditism* (bisexualism). After addition of one of the sex hormones the sex in many animals can be modified and even reversed, a fact which shows that normally one sex is only dominant and the other only recessive. This shows also that the functions and characters of sex are caused not only by differences in the gene system, but also by the balance of sex hormones, and are hence partly determined by hormone-producing genii. A *monoecious* tree (in which flowers with stamens and pistils occur on the same plant) may in this way change into a *dioecious* tree (in which the two kinds of flowers occur on different plants).

Although we know that ordinary physical causes are responsible for changes (mutations) in plants and animals, it seems impossible to explain the evolution of life as due *exclusively* to such causes. The phenomena of life are so complex and require such a high degree of organization and cooperation, that random changes, even with the highest degree of selection, seem entirely insufficient to explain life and its development on the earth. Mutations seem to represent *new combinations* of given characteristics, or *losses* of such characteristics, or an *increase* or *decrease* in their degree of manifestation, and it seems to the writer inconceivable that entirely *new* properties can be produced in this way.

There is no known physical process by which an inorganic structure, however complex, can be induced to show reproductive properties of the type characteristic of cells and genes. Even if it were possible to split an inorganic structure into two equal parts, its activities in the case of even the simplest organism must be coordinated in order to secure assimilation of new substance and elimination of waste products, since life is eminently a dynamic and well ordered process, requiring energy and chemical transformations for its normal functioning.   Many chemical substances are sensitive to light, but the change from a sensitive ganglion on the skin to a complex optical organ like an eye is so tremendous that we can not conceive of it as being due to random changes, directed by selection.   Further, an optical organ must be associated with a nervous system and a brain capable of giving rise to that mysterious element in our consciousness which we call *vision*.   It is also inconceivable that the higher mental faculties like feeling, thoughts and logical reasoning are products of chance combinations of atoms.   It is significant that new forms of life have appeared on earth rather suddenly, and that both ancient and modern organic life is represented by *standard types* and *species* of organisms, instead of by a more uniform sequence of living forms, as might be expected if the change had been more gradual.[1]   It is no wonder that some authorities in biology are now convinced that mutations are insufficient to explain the origin of life and the more radical changes in evolution.

[1] Cf. Bateson, Science, *55*, 55, 1922.   Presidential Address, Brit. Ass. for the Adv. of Science, 1914.

The writer believes that the fundamental problem of evolution is the same as that of the origin of life, of mind, and of matter. It would be useless to discuss the problem of the ultimate origin of matter or of anything else. We know that atoms can be changed into others (transmutations), and there are certain reasons for believing that the original matter in the universe was of a very simple kind. We shall now assert that, *as the matter in the earth is part of the original matter in the universe, so the life on the earth is part of the original life in the universe.*

Arrhenius some thirty years ago revived the old theory that the first life came to earth in the form of simple spores (panspermia), which travelled in the empty space of the universe and were propelled by light pressure. Lundmark has modified this theory and regards the meteors as carriers of some simple forms of living organisms. In the light of what we have said before, we must then assume either that all the potentialities of life in the highest organisms were incorporated in these simple organisms (the theory of "unfoldment"), or that later additions of living elements have been incorporated. We have learned about the many hereditary elements in living organisms, and there seems to be no necessity for assuming that all the characters of present-day life were involved in the first organisms on the earth.

Living cells contain many genes and genii as elementary parts. We are here particularly interested in the hereditary elements in the germ cells, and we shall denote the genes and the genii in a fertilized ovum by the collective term *ova genes*.

We shall now give the previous assertion the following more definite form:

Ova genes of many kinds exist in cosmical space. They have conveyed the elementary hereditary characters to the living organisms on the earth. They can exist and can retain their properties, even when they are not associated with matter.

The reasons for making the first two assertions are fairly obvious. We may picture inorganic matter as becoming organized by genes and genii, and living spores and cells as making their first appearance on earth when conditions had become suitable for life. Additional ova genes were incorporated in the germ plasm, giving muscles and bones, a spinal column and a skull, a beating heart, a nervous system and a brain to the developing organism. Consciousness appeared as mental sensations of vision, hearing, smell, and touch, also as feelings of pain and pleasure. The mechanism or organ for conscious and subconscious memory was incorporated. The genes for feeling of affection for their offspring was absorbed in the germ plasm of the early birds and mammals. Finally the power of thought and of logical reasoning was transmitted to certain animals, which then acquired supremacy over all the other animals on the earth.

The general and the subordinate genii must be regarded as entities having a *unitary* character. In the before mentioned case of the transfer of a piece of the dorsal lip of the blastopore to a developing gastrula and the formation of a secondary embryo, it was shown that the two general genii were actually *competing* with one another in the organization of the same cell material. In a similar way two *different* genii may both tend to impose their different types of organization on the same cell material. Ordinarily this causes the death of the embryo, but sometimes the result is a "mixed" plant or animal (a "chimaera"). We may think of this being the case when the fore legs and the tails of the reptiles were being converted into the wings and tail feathers of the birds. The balance of the activating hormones may for a time oscillate back and forth; the environmental conditions would by natural selection ultimately determine the outcome of the struggle. When a genie is steadily declining it soon becomes so "weak" that it can no longer be "revived," even if its reappearance would be of distinct advantage to the animal. Traces of it are left as rudimentary organs or as vestigial, useless, or modified, bones, but the organizing genie which they formerly served has seemingly disappeared completely. Remnants of old and lost genii often appear in embryonic development as a partial "recapitulation" of the life history of the race. The time sequence is in this case a direct evidence that we are dealing with structures having both time and space properties.

Dollo's law of irreversibility in organic evolution states that a lost organ or faculty can not be resurrected from its remnants. This fact strongly suggests that new organs or faculties can not be acquired gradually. If the organ is to appear again, it must be incorporated by sexual or non-sexual transfer (later to be described in connection with the explanation of mimicry), or else the genie *must be absorbed* DE NOVO *from Cosmos itself.*[1]

The conclusion to which we come is that the gradual development of a new organ or faculty is a manifestation of the incorporation of a new genie in the germ plasm of one or more individuals. The new organ or faculty is revealed by its gradual *unfoldment* in successive generations. If the organ is later lost, its fragments may remain as genes and subordinate genii, which are activated by hormones produced by genii with structural and functional properties different from those of the lost genie.

Organic life is a combination of *Living Elements*. These elements are of a more complex type than that represented by the atoms of the chemical elements, but fundamentally they are of similar nature.

[1] Cf. p. 221.

It has often been said that the genes are the "atoms" which transmit hereditary characters. This analogy now appears very far-reaching, indeed. Genes can be split, atoms can be ionized; as said before these processes may well be of somewhat similar nature. Genes form complex groups with non-uniform distribution of electric charge. These groups are the chromosomes, which are thus analogous to molecules. Groups of genes can be exchanged between homologous chromosomes. Such groups are analogous to the radicals, which are transferred as units in many chemical transformations. Certain gene groups are linked together more strongly than others, they represent the stronger electric bonds in chemical compounds. An atomic nucleus has a positive charge and is surrounded by negative electric charges; the proteins in the colloidal state have electric charges distributed in a complex pattern in the interior and over the surface. Atoms are built of *material* elements (neutrons, positrons, and electrons) joined together and organized into a space-time pattern by a non-living, immaterial space-time structure, the meshes of which are defined by the quantum of action. "Living atoms" are built of molecules (e.g. amino acids), which are assumed to be joined together and organized into a space-time pattern by a *living*, immaterial space-time structure. There are strong reasons to believe that the space-time aspect of the "spirit of atoms" is related to the corresponding aspect of the

"Spirit of the Universe." [1]   There may well be an
intimate relation between *the mental properties of
the living elements* in the universe and the *mental
properties of Cosmos,* a subject we shall study in the
next chapter.

The third assertion made is that the immaterial
essence of the ova genes can exist and can retain its
properties of transmitting hereditary characters even
when not associated with any matter.   This assertion
is not quite necessary for the understanding of the
origin and evolution of life on earth, since material
ova genes may have been transmitted to the earth in
single or multiple form (as panspermia or in meteors), but it is of great importance for the theory
of survival of memories and of the soul, which will
later be presented.

There are many reasons for the belief that genii
and gene spirits are in a high degree independent of
the incorporated matter.   As an example we may
think of a gastrula genie.   It was defined as the
wave system which determines the transformation
of a morula into a gastrula.   Structures of this type
are easy to recognize when there is not too much yolk
in the egg cell, and they are characteristic for the
embryonic development in all animals except sponges
and Protozoa.   The chemical composition and the

[1] This statement expresses the modern theory that the metrical
properties of cosmical space-time are related to the properties and
to the number of atoms in the universe.

molecular structure of the cell substance may evidently vary from one animal to another, but the matter must be fluid enough to follow the changing structure of the gastrula genie. When a gastrula is killed, for instance by the addition of an inorganic foreign substance which acts as a poison, the movements of the cells are suddenly stopped and the matter soon changes to simpler chemical compounds. What has happened to the gastrula genie? This marvelous wave system together with all the genii attached to it has apparently disappeared without leaving a trace. When electric and magnetic fields are modified they reappear somewhere else in some form or other. If the fields inside the atoms are modified they reappear as photons and radiation which carry frequency, momentum, and energy from one atomic system to another. The gastrula genie is not an ordinary electro-magnetic structure, its properties are not due to the molecular structure of the cell substance, and the cells seem to follow passively the changing wave system. An expanded gastrula genie is not associated with any particular atoms or molecules, and, as transplantation experiments have shown, not even with any particular cell or cell group. In fact, all evidence indicates that the gastrula genie is associated with the gastrula as a whole. It seems incredible that such a well defined wave system which had so pronounced integral properties and which was so tenacious of life and so little de-

pendent on the individual cells should simply disappear when a non-living foreign substance was
added. Perhaps it is not completely gone? Perhaps
the poison was simply a "negative" hormone which
absorbed the energy in the living wave system, but
left the fundamental source intact? Perhaps there
are special conservation laws for living sources as
there are such laws for non-living sources?

From such considerations and from evidence of
different kinds the writer has come to the following
conclusions. Genii can not be annihilated. When an
eggcell, an embryo, or an animal dies the living
wave systems in the genii contract to such an extent
that the latter are reduced to transcendental, energy-
free sources which are no longer linked to space and
time. The sources can be unattached to matter, and
they appear then to us as if they were dispersed into
interstellar space. They have restitutional properties
which can not be ˙expressed in terms of our conceptual space and time. The gene spirits have properties similar to those of genii. Different gene spirits
and genii have different degrees of stability and restitutional power.

Certain facts about *viruses* have recently been discovered which can be explained as due to a transfer
of gene spirits. Viruses are substances which can
transmit certain diseases, but they differ from, bacteria in the fact that the active elements can not be seen
even in the most powerful optical microscopes, and

these elements can pass through very fine filters. Stanley has found that certain viruses consist of large protein molecules consisting of a very great number of atoms, in other words we can regard them as very small complex *crystals* of definite mass and size. A crystal suggests non-living material, but these protein crystals can apparently reproduce themselves very quickly when they come into contact with certain cells and tissues. If we illuminate the active virus with ultraviolet light or expose it to sound of extremely high frequency, it loses its power of reproduction, but there is no noticeable change in the molecular structure. The virus studied by Stanley in some cases automatically changed its properties and produced a somewhat different disease. Apparently it had suffered a change similar to those which have been called "mutations."

Opinions differ whether we should regard viruses as living or non-living matter. The introduction of living immaterial structures makes it less difficult to understand the phenomena here described. We may regard a virus as a *gene-carrying substance;* the active molecules or crystals are proteins organized by and still combined with gene spirits. The inactive crystals are organized proteins from which the gene spirits have been "shaken out." The former must be regarded as living proteins, the latter as dead proteins, since one of the fundamental properties of "living elements" is that of being able, when in their non-expanded form, to reproduce their own structure by a process of splitting.[1]

Active viruses are probably a collection of living genes, without any genii to organize them into cells or more complex structures. When the active substance comes in contact with certain living cells, the amino-acids in the cytoplasm of the cells are reorganized by the virus genes. The amount of active substance is then quickly increased by reproduction of virus genes, the material being taken from the cell substance. The cells die from lack of nourishment or from poisoning, and the plant or animal is killed or becomes stunted in its growth.

Although in this case the genes are certainly not free from atoms or electrons during their passage through a dense porcelain filter—which at least in some cases must temporarily disrupt the protein crystals—this phenomenon may well serve as an example of a transfer of gene spirits to non-organized amino acids. Since the gene spirits have not "expanded" they can be regarded as having the same properties as ova genes.

Mimicry among insects, sea-horses, and some other

---

[1] Svedberg and his associates in Upsala have found that certain classes of proteins are built from standard protein molecules of very large molecular weight. These protein molecules must be regarded as non-living matter, since they do not show reproductive properties. In no case has it hitherto been possible to produce even the simplest *living* protein molecules from inorganic material.

animals may perhaps be explained as absorption of immaterial ova genes. Let us imagine a larva covering itself with a leaf for protection during its pupa stage. During the following metamorphosis a new general genie with its system of subordinate genii is in the present theory assumed to expand and to cause a progressive reorganization of the material in the cells, a process which manifests itself as the growth of a new nerve system with its multitude of interconnected neurones and ganglia. A very active immaterial living structure seems to be at work. When its activity is at its peak, the process must be completely dominated by it, and it is also known to be rather sensitive to external disturbances. The reproductive organs are developed during this transformation, and we may well imagine gene spirits from dying cells in the *leaf* moving into the body of the pupa and becoming attached to the immaterial structure in the reproductive organs. *Immaterial* genes and genii can well be expected to retain their properties even during the intense activities in the "melting pot" of the pupa, a "pot" that follows the expanding system of genii. After a time the matter is completely reorganized, and the pupa has become a butterfly. It lays eggs which develop into new butterflies, having wings with a pattern that closely resembles the general structure of the leaf. This type of imitation is favored by natural selection, since the new kind of butterflies can blend with its surroundings and is hence overlooked by the birds in their search for food.

Insects can adopt different disguises, larvae can resemble twigs, butterflies can imitate other species distasteful to their own enemies, and flies can imitate bees and wasps which are avoided by the birds. Such transformations can be explained by the presence of foreign genes and genii during the development of the reproductive organs. The transformations can not be acquired in many stages, they must be transmitted in more or less complete form, otherwise we could never understand some of them.

We know that genes and genii have different degrees of stability, since certain hereditary characters can be more changed by physical disturbances than others. Sometimes a genie may be modified and remain so for many generations, then suddenly revert to its original form. The structure may have been disturbed or incomplete, but it seems to have an innate power of restitution.

Individual genes are in general invisible to the eye. In the centrosomes, of which we have spoken before, we have entities which carry the mechanism of cell division as a hereditary character, and for this reason we may well regard them as a particular kind of genes, residing, not like other genes in the chromosomes, but in the cytoplasm of the cells. The centrosomes we see in living, unstained cells are probably "liquid crystals," and the images seem to be formed by refraction [1] rather than by scattering of light. It has been found that the viscosity of the cytoplasm is different in the "rays" from the centrosomes from what it is in the regions between the rays. It seems that the fields in the centrosomes are able to line up the polar molecules in the cytoplasm in long strings, thus causing a "gel" condition (fibrous molecular structure) along definite paths. To the writer it seems evident that we have a complex immaterial structure in the center of the centrosomes (the *centrioles*), capable of orienting polar molecules and organizing them into living, material genes or micro-organisms. The rays of centrosomes extend when cell division begins and seem to push the chromosomes into the equatorial plane. Later the rays contract and pull in the half chromosomes. This behavior indicates that gene spirits can *contract* as well as *expand*, a contention supported by other evidence.

In the transformation of half embryos into complete ones we witnessed the disintegration of a molecular pattern and the formation of a new structure. The cause of the disintegration could only be that the original pattern was no longer sustained by any living source and wave system and the normally acting disruptive forces could then freely perform their work.

---

[1] Refraction phenomena can best be studied if the illumination is produced by a point source of light, in which case the images are not blurred or obliterated.

They were, however, soon superseded by the organized forces of the new expanding wave systems associated with the two new sources. (The same kind of phenomena may well occur in the simple case of the transformation of a system of rays from a single centrosome into a double system sustained by two centrosomes.) As we have said before it is impossible to picture the division of a complex wave system into two parts of which each one is equivalent to the original one. The division of genes and genii must involve *all* their properties, including the mental characteristics described in the next chapter, and physical space has not enough "dimensions" for such a profound process which must even transcend the physical world. It is necessary to assume that previous to the division of genes and genii the corresponding living wave systems have *completely* disappeared, and that at the very moment of their division the sources have actually lost their association with space and time. This gives us an important clue to the fundamental nature of *death*. We should hence expect that during cell division the chromosomes go through a cycle of *splitting*,[1] *expansion* and *contraction*.[2] If the

---

[1] This splitting does not take place in physical space and the new sources can have no initial separation because this can only be defined in the presence of a wave structure. With the development of their wave systems the sources separate, and what we may call *The Exclusion Principle for Living Elements* becomes effective.

[2] After this was written (in 1938) Buck and Boche at the Biological Laboratory of the Carnegie Institution of Washington

proper hormones are present the new "free," "un-bound" or "transcendental" sources begin to develop their wave systems so quickly that they are immediately chained to the world of atoms and molecules, in other words, they are *reborn*. Our conclusions can now be stated in the following form:

During cell division certain living elements die, which means that they lose their wave systems and hence their association with the physical world of space and time. They are immediately reborn in duplicate form and are then reincarnated in the world of atoms and molecules.

When a living element is associated with material particles of any sort it can not have completely lost its wave system, because this is the connecting link between the living source and the matter waves of the particles. If there are not enough molecules of the right kind (e.g. proteins in solution) available or if the necessary hormones (e.g. oxygen in solution) are not present, the wave system may be greatly contracted. Such living elements would act as a virus, and many viruses may be of this type. Let us assume that a living element is not associated with any

have found direct evidence for this contraction and expansion. They studied the giant chromosomes in the salivary glands of certain insects, which chromosomes are several thousand times larger than those in the other cells of the body. If the air around the *living* chromosomes is replaced by nitrogen or carbon dioxide the chromosomes contract greatly, and they regain their gigantic size in the presence of oxygen, which seems to act as a "hormone" for the whole chromosome system. (*The Collecting Net*, Vol. XIII, No. 8, 1938).

atoms or electrons at all but still retains a vestigial wave system. It is then still "alive" since it is linked to space-time. If living elements can exist in this form their wave system can be expected to act as pilot waves, and in a vacuum they should travel with the velocity of light. Such dormant living elements would then appear to us as "living photons." There are certain reasons to believe that living elements occasionally are set free in this form and they may play an important role in the dissemination of life in the universe. They should, however, not be regarded as the ultimate origin of life, which lies, I believe, in the realm beyond space and time in which domain our mental attributes have their ultimate origin and their association.

Because gene spirits and genii completely separated from atoms probably always are in the contracted form and hence can not be directly observed, it is not surprising that we have as yet no direct evidence for their existence in this form. Gene spirits and genii carry probably no electric charges, hence they are as difficult to observe as are radio waves and pilot waves. It is only by their direct effect on *material* elements that we can become aware of their existence and study their properties.[1]

---

[1] Although immaterial structures do not appreciably affect light beams and hence are "invisible," they should, however, deflect beams of slow-moving electrons, an effect which can be regarded as an incomplete capture. We can thus say that such structures should, in their expanded form, be observable by the use of the electron microscope.

Experiments could be made to investigate the eventual transfer of virus genes from one culture medium to another, under conditions such that no transfer of atoms or electrons can occur. As we said before gene spirits may well have different degrees of stability, and some of them may possibly be partly converted into radiation, in which case we would get different types of mutation.

During the past few years evidence has been found which indicates that the effect of a gene depends upon its location in the chromosome ("position effects"). From our standpoint this is not surprising. The space-time aspect of a gene is a stationary wave system. In combination with other similar wave systems it forms a wave system of a higher order (a chromosome), and its properties depend upon its relation to adjacent gene spirits. A "wave" as such has no individuality, its appearance being greatly influenced by other waves, particularly by those having similar wave lengths.

A musical tone can be produced by a tuning fork, but its effect on a melody depends upon its relation to other tones. The individual tones and their corresponding air vibrations merge into the melody and the general vibration. A chromosome is like a "melody"; some tones (genes) are "amplified" during embryonic development in one part of the body and other tones in other parts. The amplifying system is the system of genii, and the amplifiers themselves are certain types of hormones which probably act by resonance effects as in a musical instrument.

The ova genes may have come to the earth as individuals or in groups; expressed in the language of music they may have come as tones, as tunes, as melodies, or as a symphony.   In the next chapter some reasons will be given which indicate that they have come, and still are coming, as a symphony, but the first "resonators" (molecules) on the earth were only able to respond to simple tones or tunes of the cosmic symphony which vibrated throughout space. Gradually resonators developed which could reproduce many tunes of the music.   A certain group of animals, which we call *men*, responded to and reproduced some important accords in the symphony.   But the human reproduction of the cosmic music is only an imperfect, incomplete, and often disharmonious imitation of the celestial symphony.

Some time ago I visited a biological station in Southern California.   In an aquarium were fishes and crabs, sea anemones and sea cucumbers, and other strange creatures of the ocean.   There was also an octopus which fascinated me with his strange shape, his unusual way of walking, and his mysterious, almost human eyes.[1]   He looked like a curious being

[1] The eyes of an octopus like those of other cephalopod molluscs differ in some respects from the eyes of the vertebrates.   In the former the lids serve as a pupil, there are two corneas, the outer one being perforated and the inner one dividing the lens into an inner and an outer section.   In the cephalopods the optic

from another part of the universe. I realized that his strangeness *was* due to his coming from a "distant world"—distant in both space and time if expressed in human measures.

He was in a sense at least five hundred million years old. And I had acquired the same eyes as he had—and I felt convinced that they had come from the same original cosmic source.

nerve is entirely behind the retina and the nerve ends are facing the light, while in the vertebrates the optic nerve pierces the retina and the nerve ends are turned back, away from the incoming light. In the vertebrates the retina and the optic cup are formed from brain substance, in the cephalopods the eyes are formed directly from the ectoderm of the gastrula. Using the terminology of this book we may say that eyes consist of elementary parts (each with ganglia and a sensitive nerve end) coordinated by the "genie of the eye" and that this genie in man is a "mutation" of that in the octopus. The usual explanation in terms of a "convergent evolution" of different kinds of eyes into similar end products appears to the writer extremely improbable. If the explanation of mimicry here given is the true one, it is possible that the vertebrates have acquired their present eyes from the cephalopods by transfer of immaterial genii of the eye to their germ plasm, the elementary organs of vision being already present.

Mind and Matter

ONE PROBLEM, perhaps more than any other, has always puzzled philosophers. The problem is the relationship of mind to matter. Much has been written about it, but to a great extent it has remained unsolved.

Let us give an example. In physics we learn that light is a wave motion of some sort. Formerly it was thought that we had to do with a material substance, called *ether*, in which oscillations occurred corresponding to the color of frequency of light. This analogy had developed from observations of sound waves in air, where the frequency of vibration corresponds to the pitch of the sound. Later investigations revealed that light not only has properties similar to waves, but also to particles, now called photons. Whatever conception we have of light, there is no doubt that it represents a kind of "electromagnetic radiation," which strikes our eyes. It may be light reflected from some surface or emitted by a glowing object like the filament in an electric lamp. The light is refracted in the eye-lens and the crystalline body, and an image is formed on the retina in the rear portion of the eye. The phenomenon is very similar to what we see in a photographic camera, when we let the image fall on a translucent screen at a certain distance from the objective. In the retina are *rods* and *cones* on which the image falls, and which are in some way sensitive to light. We may imagine that chemical changes take place under the influence of light, very similar to those that take place in a photographic film.[1] The rods and the cones are at the end of nerve fibers with ganglia and the nerve fibers are joined in a bundle called the *optic nerve*, which crosses the similar bundle of nerves from the other eye and goes to a certain part of the brain in the back of the head. The brain is made of cells, containing the same genes as the rest of the body, and yet different in certain ways. The brain contains an extremely large number of neurones with their nerve fibers.

And then a "miracle" happens. We "see light," not as a general glow, but as a distinct image. And we see all the colors of the rainbow distributed in a definite way in the picture. The physical phenomenon, *radiation*, has been converted into a mental phenomenon, *vision*. Is there any way to explain this wonder? Can we obtain the slightest understanding of the connection between the physical phenomena

[1] The image on the retina of the eye can be "fixed," as a photographic plate is fixed, by plunging the eye into a solution of alum immediately after death.

on the one hand, and the mental phenomena on the other?

Other examples might be given of the connection between mind and matter. Vibrations in the air are converted into noise or musical sound in our consciousness. The hammering of atoms against our skin (heat motion) is perceived as tactual sensation or as a feeling of heat or pain. Vapors cause chemical changes in the membranes of our noses, and we perceive a smell or a fragrance. Chemical substances in solution give us a taste in our consciousness.

All these phenomena we are accustomed to call *sensations*. They are made possible by peculiar combinations of our sense organs, our nervous system, and our brain. They impart to us signals and information from an external world common to all observers.

Then too we have *feelings*, like happiness and sorrow, love and hatred in our consciousness, which are in some mysterious way connected with chemical and electrical processes in our brain and our nervous system.

Feelings are often influenced by *ideas*, induced by spoken words through our organs of hearing, or by written words, as when you read a book.

We have also a *will*. We may consciously and deliberately give signals *from* the brain to our nervous system and these signals are carried to certain muscles in our body, which then contract—and we move our arms or legs. The will may also be subconscious, the signals do not pass through the cortex of the brain, but are relayed by other channels to our muscles. Thus the beating of the heart goes on without any conscious activity of our brain.

The fact is sufficiently emphasized that we are dealing with two kinds of phenomena, *physical* and *mental*, the corresponding entities of which are usually referred to as *matter* and *mind*. Between the two phenomena or entities there is a gap—a curtain always pulled down, precluding our efforts at further investigation.

Philosophers have advanced four main theories to explain the relationhip between mind and matter. First, there may be two entities in the world, matter and mind, which sometimes come into "contact" with one another; secondly, there may be only matter, mind and mental phenomena being strange products of matter and motion; thirdly, everything may be mind, and matter may be more or less of an illusion; or, fourthly, we may be dealing with two aspects of the same phenomena, the physical aspect and the mental aspect.

Let us try to find the correspondence between the physical and the mental aspect of "light," selecting as an example the color *red*. Physically red is associated with an electro-magnetic radiation of a wave length around 0.00065 millimeters (a forty thousandth part of an inch), or, probably better expressed, with something that vibrates with a frequency of about 450 million million periods per second. From a mental standpoint it can be characterized simply as red light, a sensation which we shall assume is the same for all people who possess similar sense organs and whose gene systems are not modified by some form of color blindness.

We have said before that ordinary color blindness (inability to distinguish between red and green) is due to a defect in the gene system contained in the X-chromosomes. Red is hence a quality which requires for its realization in our consciousness the existence of certain hereditary factors, and the absence of these factors precludes our realization of the existence of the color we designate by the term red.

Where do colors come from? As the pain does not reside in the needle that pricks us, or sea sickness in the waves that move us up and down, so color sensations do not as such originate in the external objects we believe exist around us. These objects emit or reflect electro-magnetic radiation of certain wave lengths, and this radiation seems to give rise to the mental sensation of color. The change from radiation to color is not comparable to ordinary physical or chemical transformations. In these transformations one substance may be changed into another with a different structure, light may ionize certain atoms in a photographic plate, or radio waves may produce electric currents which act on a membrane and set the air in vibration. In all such cases we are dealing with a change of one space-time structure into another, or rather with a causal chain of space-time phenomena as they appear in the shadow world of our direct vision or in our everyday or scientific mental imagery. The transformation of radiation into color is of a more profound type. The radiation, or rather the chemicals produced by it, seems *to open the gate to an entirely new realm, the realm of colors.* This realm is not characterized by its space and time properties, it appears to be as fundamental as space-time itself. As the space-time properties of the individual atoms do not arise spontaneously but are connected with the space and time properties of the universe as a whole, so the world of colors can not emerge spontaneously through a property of the nerve cells in our eyes or in our brain—it is rather a particular aspect of Cosmos comparable with its space-time aspect. The *gate* to the new domain is in the nerve cells of the observer, but the domain itself is beyond him and his brain. The colors spring from a fount which is not "here" or "there"; it flows everywhere in the universe. Our ordinary conceptions of space and time should not be applied to this world-transcending source.

Generalizing this idea we arrive at the following hypothesis. *Our sensations and other mental attributes are not byproducts of atomic configurations in each individual brain, they have a cosmic foundation and ultimate origin common to all individuals.* In the following we shall find more arguments in support of this theory, which has been vaguely expressed by many students, although it has not been given the serious attention it deserves.

The genes and genii, which are the hereditary factors determining our physical characters and mental characteristics, now appear in a new light. To our organ of sight and in our mental imagery they appear as wave systems or space-time structures. But they are *more* than that. The essence of the living entities is their *sources* which spring from and lead to a world beyond space and time. These entities connect plants and animals, their cells and their organs, their life and their mind with the *Soul of the Universe,* which projected in the human mind obviously must appear as something "mental."

The sensation of red may now be described in the following way. We have an image on the retina of the eye of a "red" object. Certain rods or cones are affected chemically (photo-electric effects); a chemical or electric state (there is fundamentally no distinction) travels first to the ganglia in the retina and then along the bundle of fine nerve fibers to the back of the brain. The electric or chemical state in the nerves acts as a hormone does and activates one or many of the genes [1] for red color. Other substances

[1] When here and in the following the terms genes and genii are used, these entities are supposed to exist in their "expanded"

carried by the blood also appear to be necessary for this activation.

But what does the "activation" of these particular genes mean? We must remember that what we have described until now are phenomena, which can in principle be observed by our senses aided by instruments like microscopes and galvanometers. They are important in themselves for our understanding of the universe, but they represent only the space-time aspect of these phenomena.

We can only describe the relation between the microcosmos in the genes and the macrocosmos in the universe by symbolic analogies. We may say that the genes of red vision in the eyes or the brain were parts of, or had an intimate association or correspondence with, the "redness in the World Soul." The activation made the association effective, and the color red appeared in the consciousness of the observer. It would not be quite appropriate to say that the genes were "in tune" with the redness of the universe, for the word "in tune" implies a numerical correspondence, and red is not characterized by any number or group of numbers, although the corresponding electro-magnetic radiation is so characterized in space and time.

form, as differentiated tissues and particularly as neurones. The term gene has in the following been used in many cases in which the term genie would be more appropriate because we are in general dealing with the concerted action in extended fields containing many activated neurones.

I realize well that we have not explained the sensation of color. But we have gained something. We can better understand the cause of the common perception of many individuals, when receiving the same or similar stimuli from the external world around them. The consciousness of the individual has become part of a more general consciousness. Such generalizations are not foreign to scientific reasoning, in which the number of independent assumptions must always be reduced to a minimum.

Recently some new evidence has been uncovered which makes it almost necessary for us to regard mental phenomena as transcending physical space. The investigations by Rhine and his associates at Duke University have shown the reality[1] of the phenomena of *telepathy* (transfer of thoughts and mental pictures) and *clairvoyance* (seeing at a distance without use of the eyes). Most people appear to have a rudimentary sense in this direction, others have it somewhat more developed, and the higher degrees of development or activation appear to be hereditary. According to Rhine the faculties can be measured with high precision and are greatly reduced

[1] After this was written, several psychologists have expressed doubts about the validity of Rhine's conclusions. Even if it ultimately should be shown that his results are not conclusive and that telepathy and clairvoyance are not normal phenomena, there is a very great number of perfectly well established definite cases for which no other explanation seems possible. To ignore such evidence is deliberately to overlook a most important clue to the nature of mental phenomena in general.

by certain drugs and enhanced by others, and the two faculties always appear together and are similarly affected by the same drugs. It makes no difference whether the distance to the "observed" object is 10 feet or 250 miles. Obstructions have no effect, neither has the position of the objects in relation to the "observer."

To understand such phenomena of extra-sensory vision it is clear that we must enter a field beyond that of the space and time employed in the science of physics. In a crude way this type of vision has been pictured as a "going out" by an individual mind into a new territory to which the ordinary limitations of space are not applicable. For practical purposes we have developed to a high degree of perfection certain sense organs, while those of other types have been of little use to us and have not been developed by natural selection, although they may be better developed among certain animals, e. g. migratory birds, carrier pigeons, and termites. The absence of space limitation in the case of extra-sensory perception is a new argument in favor of the assertion that our genes of vision are associated with fundamental cosmic attributes—and from these cosmic attributes I believe that colors and sound, harmony and music, thoughts and ideas emanate.

We can now proceed in our study of the relation between physical and mental phenomena, gradually progressing from the simpler and better known to the more complex and less known relations and phenomena.

There are probably a great number of elementary color sensations, and each one will be regarded as represented by a gene in a gene group—which we shall call the *color genes*—which in potential form exists in every living cell of the body, and in developed form in the optic ganglia in the retina and in certain neurones in the rear part of the brain. In the preceding chapter reasons were given for the assumption that the genes and the genii originally came from Cosmos itself. As the workers in a termitary seem to retain mental contact with their common mother, the queen, so the color genes seem to have retained their connection with their world transcending ultimate source. The optic ganglia are probably excited by resonance effects produced by chemical hormones interacting with the living wave system in the nerve cells. As the expansion of the general genie is usually manifested by the opening up of nerve channels which previously had no space extension, so potential channels to a "nerve center" or rather to a new "dimension" of Cosmos are opened up during the exitation. The gate to the "realm of colors" is temporarily left ajar—and we have a glimpse in our consciousness of the corresponding pre-existing color qualities in the World Soul, Cosmic Consciousness, Cosmos, God, or whatever term the reader may prefer.

When only one color gene is activated we see a nearly "pure" color. If two different color genes are activated at the same time, we have the same sensation, as when another color gene is activated. Thus when the "green" and the "violet" radiation affect the retina at about the same time the perception is blue, which color belongs to a gene, which can also be activated by radiation corresponding to the blue color. Yellow and red give the same sensation as orange; yellow and indigo give blue; and red and greenish blue give white. When radiation representing all the spectral colors reach the eye at about the same time and in a certain proportion with regard to intensity, we see white light. The color "white" is here regarded as a mental quality similar to other colors, not as a compounded mental quality. The basis for this assumption lies, of course, in the simultaneous perception of two or more kinds of radiation as a new one.[1]

[1] The color sensations are generally regarded as derived from three fundamental colors, and, in case of ordinary color blindness, only from two. This applies, however, only to the color sensations which depend on the action of the cones. In the central part of the retina are only cones, while further out the rods become more and more numerous, and at the edge of the sensitive part of the retina there are only rods. The latter are activated by a chemical substance, the visual purple. They respond to weak light and represent gray or colorless vision, which would seem to indicate that we have genes (ganglia) for the perception of white as an elementary color, although other explanations are also possible. The visual purple contains vitamin A, and it is the absence of this vitamin which is the usual cause of night blindness. (*Continued on next page*)

The most remarkable fact of our sense of vision is the perception of a spatial distribution of colors. We do not in general see a flash of red or blue light, we see a colored *picture* with remarkable details. This fact makes the sense of vision extremely valuable to men and animals; it is of more practical importance to us than any of our other senses. The spatial separation is primarily due to the distribution of light on the rods and cones of the retina; in general the different rods and cones are illuminated with different kinds of radiations. Each cone and rod is connected with ganglia and sends its impulses to the back of the brain.

The sensation of spatial separation, that is, of an extended detailed image, will be regarded as being brought about by the activation of certain genes in many adjacent nerve cells. We may call these genes the *space-genes*. The capability of perceiving space by sight, by touch, or by hearing, and in some animals even by smell, is certainly inherited. In Cosmos it seems to represent extension and separation into distinct parts, a quality with which our space-genes can come into contact, when they are activated by impulses from the sense organs.

The other sense organs and the sensations they

The effect of color combinations can possibly be explained by assuming that different mixtures of radiation can by chemical action produce the same hormones, as in the case of a combined "green" and "violet" radiation which may produce the same chemical reaction as "blue" radiation.

represent in our consciousness can now be understood. There are sound genes, smell-genes, heat-genes, cold-genes, and taste-genes, and some others. In Cosmos there are sounds of different pitch, smells and fragrances, heat and cold, taste, and pain. This may sound fantastic, but we must be consistent and logical in our deductions.

The perception of time is probably also carried by genes. All conscious beings have such a perception. It is intimately connected with consciousness itself, for all conscious phenomena or activities are "now" or "then." The corresponding quality in Cosmos seems to be change and increase in disorganization (entropy) in a particular direction which we call "forward." In the living world there is also reorganization and a special kind of physical and mental development in the forward direction of time.

In order that a mental picture may become what it appears to be, we need not only preexistent *mental elements* from which it can be built, but also some kind of *mental framework* or space-time structure in which the elements can be incorporated, since otherwise the elements would be mixed with one another in a haphazard way. Such a mental framework must have certain predictable space and time properties which we might be able to detect by physical observations. Since the optic nerve fibers end in different parts of an extended portion in the rear of the brain, the structure should cover this whole region. In order to record moving objects and give definite impressions in the consciousness of their speed across the field of view, the structure should be able to make a time record of the motion. It must hence have the properties of a "clock," that is, it must be associated with a vibrating system having a constant period. From our ability to distinguish between motions in opposite directions in a limited field of view, which ability is lost when an image moves across the corresponding part of the retina at so high a speed that the "mental clock" does not change perceptibly during the transit, we should expect this period to be of the order of a tenth of a second. When, due to different causes affecting the brain, our visual pictures appear to be blurred or swaying, we should expect to find temporary disturbances or changes in this framework.[1] Since the structure must coordinate the activities in many separated nerve cells in the brain, it should have the nature of a genie and be centered in neurones having automatic activity.

It is an interesting fact that in a living brain we can observe a general fluctuation in the electric potentials. Ordinarily the most prominent and regular "brain wave" in man has a period of one tenth of a second and is called the *alpha rhythm*. This brain wave is present in the waking state and gradually

[1] The writer has occasionally noticed vibratory motions with periods somewhat larger than a tenth of a second in isolated parts of the field of vision. The vibrations appear only under special conditions.

disappears during sleep.   In deep sleep it is replaced by slow, less regular brain waves with periods ranging from a half to three seconds.   In the waking state the alpha rhythm is most clearly shown under quiet conditions and in the absence of visual stimulation. As soon as light strikes the eyes, the alpha rhythm is decomposed and changed into a very complicated set of waves.   This wave system has been found to be associated with the rear portion of the brain.   The alpha rhythm disappears during abnormal conditions in the brain, as for instance during epileptic fits.

From the description of life processes presented in the preceding chapters it follows that very large changes in the space scale is a property characteristic for developing living structures in general.   In the process of activation energy seems to be imparted to the living structure, probably by resonance.   This results either in a splitting or in an expansion, and the expansion is sometimes followed by a contraction when the activation has ceased.   If we regard the alpha rhythm as a living immaterial wave system, acting on electrons in the brain, the skull, and the measuring instruments, we may picture the increased intensity of the alpha rhythm as due to an expansion of a wave system beyond its normal size.[1]   Since

[1] With very sensitive instruments we might even find nodal surfaces surrounding the rear portion of the brain and characterized by minimum intensity of the alpha rhythm.   These surfaces should quickly expand on awakening and contract when losing consciousness, and the contraction should be very slow

the expanded system is not loaded down by atoms, as is the wave system in the neurones, the slow expansion of which in the embryonic development has been accompanied by incorporation of atoms, it should be very sensitive and able to respond very quickly to nerve impulses. (We have previously called attention to the fact that nerve impulses can be detected outside the neurones and nerve fibers and that they produce *concerted* effects. This may give a clue to an understanding of the strange fact that an individual in general can not have here several different feelings and thoughts at the same time. We have become so used to this fact that we do not realize its great significance.)

It seems then that the alpha rhythm is a system of brain waves on which our color sensations, and some other classes of sensations as well, are impressed somewhat as musical tones are impressed on radio waves. There can be little doubt that the fluctuations in the electric potentials of the brain are actually centered in neurones, and it would seem that special nerve impulses and the increased oxygen supply of the brain at awakening act as hormones causing an activation and expansion of a particular wave system, that is, of a particular genie. This wave system seems thus to have the same properties as other genii, when going to sleep. According to the picture presented these surfaces represent on a magnified scale the outer portions of the immaterial living wave system in those neurones in which the alpha rhythm is centered.

and there are certain reasons for assuming that it is the physical manifestation of that particular genie which represents *our faculty of space and time co-ordination*.

Very young infants and many people even at maturity do not show evidence of any alpha rhythm, although their vision and power of perception in general are not affected by this circumstance. The amplification or expansion of the genie in question may in infants and among the people mentioned be less than normal in which event measurements by instruments outside the skull would be difficult.

We can now better understand what part the eyes and the brain play in the production of visual sensations. Sensations of light and colors may well be made possible by an organ consisting simply of an optic ganglion, like those in the retina near the end of the optic nerve fibers. These ganglia can be regarded as differentiated cells in which the color genes have expanded, thus imparting their special properties to this particular tissue. The ganglia or their associated nerve ends are activated by chemicals produced under the influence of the radiation. These chemicals act as hormones and disappear gradually after the radiation has ceased.

To obtain an image we need a lens and to get a sharp image on the retina we need a focusing device, and these parts are organized in the embryo by the genie of the eye. The elementary color sensations must be coordinated in the two dimensions of space and in the one dimension of time into a moving picture, and this is made possible by the "extensions" of the ganglia in the form of nerve fibers reaching into the organ of space and time coordination, which is located in the brain and has the nature of a genie. In this way the visual sensations can also be connected with other mental and physical processes, without which the visual sensations would be of little practical value.

As our color genes brought us into contact with some of the colors in the World Soul, so our space and time genes and their unifying genii in our brains bring us into contact with the *space and time in Cosmos*. This contact has opened up for us a great field in our every day experience and for our scientific studies, a field which we call the *physical world*. It appears in our mental world of shadows as something we call *matter* and *motion*, that is, as space-time structures governed by rules and relations, some of which, like the quantum rules of physics and the empirical rules in biology, are not due to conventions and can not be regarded as of our own making.

Space and time are mental abstractions, they are just as "mental" as the sensation of red or of pain. We always start our studies from mental elements, and, whatever mental operations we perform, the result is still a mental world. That the world of space and time, which we ordinarily call the physical or material world, for our organ of sight *appears* to be external to the observer and in most cases actually has an external counterpart, as evidenced by comparing the simultaneous sensations of several individuals, are important data in human experience. It indicates that other mental attributes, like colors, feelings, and thoughts, also may have "external" or "cosmic" counterparts. If we do not admit the existence of these counterparts for other mental attributes than those we call space and time, we must face the hopeless task of explaining how entirely new mental qualities, like thoughts, for instance, can ever emerge from a world of space and time alone.

Because of the richness in details in our visual sensations and because of the pain we sometimes feel when we come into contact with matter, we are inclined to regard the physical world as more "real" and "tangible" than the world of colors, music, and joy, for instance. But Cosmos has many aspects, which *sub specie aeternitatis* may be much more important than the physical world of space and time to which we pay so much attention.

It seems that one of the difficulties of understanding the relationship between mind and matter is due to the fact that we take concepts belonging to one aspect of Cosmos and use them in a description of other aspects to which they are not applicable. A study of the relation between mind and matter is an attempt to find an expected correspondence or parallelism between the space-time aspect of Cosmos and those other aspects of which we are consciously aware. If we want to visualize the interaction between the "physical" processes in the brain and the corresponding "mental" phenomena we may say that the living immaterial element in the neurones has on the one hand physical properties, since through its associated living wave system it can influence the position and motions of atoms and electrons, and on the other hand mental properties inherent in the "source" and indicative of its ultimate origin, and through such sources we become immediately aware of certain attributes of Cosmos. This kind of immaterial elements, which probably do not exist in inorganic matter, offers us a connecting link between what we ordinarily call physical and mental phenomena.

Cosmos must not be regarded as a combination of mental qualities, like space, time, colors, sounds, feelings, and thoughts. There are several reasons why Cosmos must be regarded as a *non-divisible, rational entity*. One is the analogy with our own souls, which have a unitary character, in spite of the complexity of our mental activities. Our bodies have also a unitary character, in spite of the diversity of the organic processes. Further, different aspects of Cosmos are related, although they appear in our minds as totally unrelated sensations. Thus, space and time are connected by a constant relation which we measure as the velocity of light *in vacuo*, a constant which appears in *all phenomena* where both space and time properties are involved. This indicates that the space and time our mind perceives are in reality partial aspects or "projections" of a higher unit, space-time.[1] Furthermore, modern theories as to the cause of inertia would indicate that when an attempt is made to move a body in a path which differs from its "natural" path in space and time, *the whole universe offers a concerted opposition*.[2] This resistance we perceive as inertia and it is measured by a number we call mass. It appears, then, that the universe is a unitary "organism," rather than a loose collection of atoms and stars.

The unitary character of Cosmos is also shown by the fact that the properties of matter are the same on earth as in the distant stellar systems—as evidenced by the spectra of distant stars—the physical laws and constants of the whole universe can in principle be determined in any corner of this vast system. Such a uniformity is inconceivable without a unifying agency that impresses its marks always and everywhere in Cosmos. I have used the term "The Soul of the Universe" to emphasize that we are dealing

[1] It is very remarkable that this concept of a four-dimensional continuum, space-time, is not only of theoretical interest for the philosophers but has also a very practical application in the Theory of Relativity. In the domain of space-time metaphysics and natural science have finally met on common ground.

[2] This origin of mass implies that, if there were no stars and nebulae, no energy would be needed to move our trains, and when they collided no damage would be done!

not only with a uniform set of physical rules and constants but also with qualities which we are accustomed to call "mental." A "soul" is in this book defined as that which gives unity to mental activities and phenomena in general.

Although the direct evidence that Cosmos has the nature of a "mental unit" or "personality" is somewhat vague, our mind is so constructed that we can never be satisfied with a Cosmos, the parts of which are entirely unrelated to one another. The wisdom we see revealed in the organization of the living world, the harmonious, uniform laws exhibited in the inorganic world, and the wonderful mental faculties we have in some mysterious way inherited, all point to the activities of an *all embracing, intelligent, unitary entity*. It is the aspects or the *attributes* of Cosmos, and not its unrelated parts, of which we are consciously aware.

We must always remember that our knowledge of the attributes of Cosmos is a fragmentary one. Our system of genes and genii makes us more conscious of some of these attributes than of others, and many cosmical attributes may well exist of which we, on account of lack of the proper genes or of the activating hormones, are as completely unaware as are the lowest animals and plants. Observations can not go beyond the categories to which they belong and can hence not give us information about phenomena for the perception of which we do not have the necessary heritage. Deductions, inspirations and unusual or incipient faculties may, however, give us some inkling of the existence and general nature of some of these attributes. But to describe them is often as difficult as to describe the colors of a flower to a blind race. Verbal descriptions or man-made instruments could never to a race without color genes reveal the experience we call a sensation of light and color.

As an example of a cosmic attribute found by deduction and not by direct mental cognition we may mention *action*, which in modern physics has a well defined meaning. It plays a great role in nature and is always an integral multiple of a small unit, the quantum of action. The idea of the fundamental nature of action has been forced upon our intellect, which has in vain protested against its acceptance as an entity, more fundamental than space and time. This instinctive attitude is due to the fact that we have genes for the perception of space and of time, but not of action. Numerically it can be handled in our mathematical expressions, which are not limited by our powers of visualization. When we try to visualize action, however, we must project it into those mental realms, for which we have inherited perceptive faculties. Action then appears either as a product [1] of a length, a velocity, and a numerical factor we call

---

[1] It is very significant that action can be represented in many ways as a product of generalized momenta and generalized coordinates.

mass, or as a product of a time interval and a quantity we call *energy.* Mass and energy are important and, as Einstein has shown, closely related quantitative concepts in physics, but we know little or nothing of their more fundamental nature and cosmic significance. It is of special interest to recall that mass and inertia seem to be connected with the universe as a whole, and that they hence really must be regarded as *cosmical attributes.*

Momentum is another cosmic attribute which our mind can only grasp by splitting it up into a product of mass and velocity. Momentum and the quantum of action determine together the size of the meshes in the structure of atoms. Since we can not observe what goes on or predict when something will happen within these meshes, something must always be missing in our physical or space-time description of the Universe, a defect which the Principle of Indeterminacy has brought to our attention. I have no doubt that what we have neglected in our description and what our mind can not comprehend, is the *Cosmic Will,* of which we shall speak in a later chapter.

After this excursion into the lofty realm of metaphysics we are prepared for some startling deductions regarding that mental faculty we call *Memory,* which is a very interesting mental phenomenon, to which special attention should be paid. It bridges the moments of time in our consciousness, as we have said in a previous chapter. Certain simple kinds of memories must be carried by ova genes, since subconscious memories of the race and of organic life in general (instincts) are hereditary characters transmitted by them.

A study of the nature of memory shows immediately that it must be carried by an immaterial structure. We accumulate in our brains memories from different periods of our life, sometimes for periods of eighty years or more. The matter in our brain is continuously changing; new atoms are incorporated in the cells, while other atoms are removed as waste products.[1] How can memory last, when we incorporate new atoms in our brain and thus have a "new" brain after a relatively short time? Here the importance and the necessity of an immaterial, living structure in the brain, independent of that of atoms, becomes immediately evident. This structure never changes, it appears to be unchanging and indestructible. It associates itself continuously with new matter, but it is still the same. But it can grow by acquisition of new experiences, and the acquisitions are themselves indestructible, perhaps for all eternity. Memories may well be eternal, but, like other stable

[1] Since neurones are not rebuilt it has sometimes been assumed that the matter in the brain does not change during the adult life of the individual. With the aid of substances which have temporarily been made radioactive, it has recently been possible to show that the atoms in the neurones, like those in other parts of the body, are quickly replaced by new ones.

structures, they can only be eternal in the forward direction of time.

Memories are built of mental elements; they are more or less like a set of pictures arranged in a definite sequence in time, each of them capable of activation and thus of appearing in a frame very similar to that of ordinary vision. Just as we had to introduce a framework for the momentary visual sensations, so we need a framework for the elementary memory elements, in order that the proper order may be preserved, both within the individual pictures and in the temporal sequence, a condition without which indescribable confusion in space and time would result. Here again a genie [1] is required, since the memory elements must form a coordinated whole, the *memory of an individual*. It may be similar to the genie which coordinated the momentary space and time perceptions; the "memory genie" seems to have *special time properties*, however, which make it victorious in the incessant struggle against the devastations of

[1] The association of memory with a genie with space-time properties does not necessarily mean that memories are definitely localized in certain brain cells. The memory genie may be visualized as a complex structure enveloping a fairly large portion of the brain, and the removal of a part of the associated matter may temporarily cause loss of activation (amnesia). Retaining a mechanical picture (which is certainly not an adequate representation), we may well imagine the memory genie as being capable of being transferred from certain cell groups to others, without any modification in its detailed structure.

time. This property of conservation or stability of structural details was one of the attributes which we previously assigned to certain living immaterial space-time structures, and it was regarded as responsible for the preservation of certain hereditary characters in animals and plants, retained during millions of years of organic evolution.

We receive many sense impressions in our life, which do not register in our consciousness. It has been shown conclusively that they are, nevertheless, registered in our subconscious mind. When this is partially awakened, in dreams, by hypnotism, or by special nervous conditions, a great wealth of sense impressions, often extraordinarily refined and detailed, can be thrown upon the screen of our consciousness, and we are amazed at our real power of perception and of memory.

When the fine-structure in the memory genie is associated with matter in the brain, it is continuously subject to the varying intense electric fields in the interior of the moving atoms and in the many neurones in the brain. It is also, like everything else, subject to violent disturbances from the cosmic radiation. Nevertheless, no actual loss of memory with age seems to occur, although sense perception and memory activation are often impaired. In other words, even the greatest known electric disturbances in a living brain seem unable to destroy the complex structure of the memory genie. The disintegration

of the brain at death causes no violent electric up-
heavals, and, if we once have admitted that the essence of immaterial space-time structures can exist
as potential "sources" completely separated from
matter, there is no reason whatsoever to think that the
memory genie is modified at death. Its stability is
probably greater than that of the spirits of the ova
genes, some of which appear to have remained unchanged during hundreds of millions of years. We
therefore conclude that there are good reasons for
the following important assertion:

*The memory of an individual is written in in-
delible script in space and time—it has become an
eternal part of a Cosmos in development.*

Spiritualistic phenomena are often difficult to
verify and even more difficult to understand, and no
opinion can here be expressed about their meaning
or value. There are two types of phenomena, however, which do not require any very unusual mental
faculties for their perception and consequently have
become generally known. If the two types of phenomena are regarded as being both of the same nature,
they indicate a survival of memories after death.
The first is that special type of telepathy in which a
person can make himself appear in the vision of another. There are many hundreds of such cases recorded and verified, and most of us have probably
had or heard about such experiences. Ordinarily the
"transmittor" of the mental picture is in a state of

mental concentration, either deliberately caused or
due to great danger or imminent or even actual death.
Seemingly the "genes for telepathic transmission"
are then abnormally activated, and the image of the
transmitting person appears in the consciousness of
one or more particular individuals. As with telepathic phenomena in general no limitation in space
seems to exist.

The other class of phenomena is the apparition of
people who have recently died or have been dead a
long time. The apparitions are often connected with
a definite place where some tragic event has occurred
and involve as a rule a repetition of past events.[1] Although such experiences are less common than those
of the previously described type, all races on earth
seem to have recorded them, and many are so well
authenticated that we have no right to doubt them.
The reason why they are usually ignored by investigators who have not themselves had any such experiences is that it seems entirely impossible to ex-

[1] An interesting case has recently been reported by Mr. Brook-
Farrar, an English artist, and G. A. Smith, an English photog-
rapher. They visited the hidden temple of *Katargama* in the
jungles of Ceylon to secure moving pictures for a travelogue. At
the temple the whole party noticed a Tamil girl dancing in the
sunlight on the steps. Quickly they set up their cameras and
filmed the whole scene. They could clearly see the girl in the
finders of their cameras. At the end of the filming the girl
disappeared. The natives evidently knew about her, but refused
to tell anything about her history. When the film was later
developed the temple stood out clearly, but *there was no trace
of the dancing girl.*

plain them scientifically. We can not ascribe them to autosuggestion since they appear unexpectedly and without any mental preparation on the part of the "observer." If we explain such strange phenomena as being produced in the same way as those of ordinary telepathy and clairvoyance, we arrive at the conclusion that what we see is a mental vision in our own consciousness similar to those seen in very vivid dreams, and that the vision more or less corresponds to the mental activities of somebody who died recently or has been dead for many years. If this type of phenomena is accepted as real, it indicates strongly that individual memories do not only persist after death, but are also capable of becoming activated, that is, of appearing in their conscious form. It also indicates that, as with ordinary memories, events connected with intense emotions are liable to become more strongly activated than others, and that the intensity and the frequency of the activation of a particular remembered event decreases with the time.

Before leaving the subject of memory we must discuss an apparent inconsistency. On the one hand we have spoken of the memory of an individual, and on the other hand we have said that mental qualities are inherent in Cosmos, that is, they are assumed to be universal. The nerve centers associated with mental activities are assumed to be *receivers* rather than independent *producers* of mental qualities. Applying this conception to individual memories we may say that the mental elements in the memory complex are universal, but their arrangement in space and time is specific for the individual. Although the memory genie is a receiver and not a producer of mental qualities, this receiver has a special structure which, when activated, arranges the mental elements in a way dependent upon the previous sensations and experiences of the individual. To the memory of an individual Cosmos supplies the "paint" and the "sound," but the individual furnishes the "canvas," the "tracing" for the painting, and the non-breakable "record."

At this point we will say something about the *Will*, to which subject we shall return in a later chapter. Some things we do unconsciously, others we do consciously, often with doubt as to the advisability of so doing. A physical aspect of will unquestionably exists, which may correspond to some physical phenomena in the brain and in certain nerve centers. But since the genes and genii are apparently the most important living parts of our body, we may well associate will with some kind of genes coordinated by a "will genie." We shall now give an example of the action of the will in connection with a complex process.

When I write something with my hand the physical process appears to be about as follows. A will-genie in a neurone is activated by a hormone and I feel that I *will* express a certain thought. Other nerve centers may also be activated, of which some may temporarily get the upper hand and I feel that I will draw a picture instead. But my reasoning tells me that I can better express my thoughts by a combination of certain words representing concepts, than I can by drawing a picture. After *deliberation* I choose the written expression rather than the pictorial, since I am a poor artist and know little about symbolic representations in space and colors. A musician may express his ideas in the form of a symphony, and he lets his will direct him to do so.

When the decision to express a certain idea has been made, I choose certain terms in a language with which I am familiar. To separate the words from the ideas they represent is practically impossible. It might be theoretically possible, but the ideas would be difficult to convey to other people by the usual means of communication. Certain expressions are tried and rejected as inadequate, redundant, or not euphonious, better expressions are adopted and written down, perhaps to be changed later.

The "writing down" is a most complex process. A complicated set of signals is sent to a part of the brain under the bulge of the forehead. There hormones can instantaneously activate the "nerve system for delicate muscular movements." Nerve impulses are sent to my right hand, delicate muscles are contracted in the proper order, and the pencil moves over the paper. Light from the sun strikes the paper and the graphite grains, an image of the script is formed on the retina, nerve impulses go to the optical center of the brain, the picture is impressed on an electromagnetic wave-system of which I am directly aware —and I see the written script on the paper and understand its meaning.

This is a very marvelous combination of activities with which we are all familiar so far as their outward appearance goes. But familiarity breeds contempt. It is well to stop occasionally and consider the many operations involved, all performed at lightning speed, —to stop in humble admiration for a wisdom that is not ours.

Feelings are now comparatively easy to understand. Many experiments have been made to establish the relation between hormones and feelings. We shall here describe a striking experiment from the animal world. In one of these experiments a female rat, at first completely oblivious to offspring offered to her for adoption, was given a few injections with *prolactin* (a pituitary hormone). Immediately she wanted to adopt as many young animals as were placed in her cage. She wanted to cherish not only infants of her own species, but also baby rabbits and even baby squabs. A normal rat would make a prompt meal of a proffered squab, and there could be no doubt that a profound change had taken place in her disposition and in her feelings towards the young animals.

If we try to follow the chain of cause and effect in this case we arrive at the following conclusion. The hormone is carried by the blood to one or more nerve centers in the brain, where a special gene or genie has "expanded" and imparted its physical properties to a cell group (cell differentiation), making it particularly sensitive to a special kind of stimulation. The hormone "stimulates" or "activates" the "gene for affection," which has not only physical properties (space-time structure), but also other more specific qualities of quite another type. This gene or genie is a part of, or has an intimate connection with, the "affection in the World Soul," and when it is activated the animal feels a conscious or subconscious urge to mother helpless infants.

As an example of *emotions* we shall take the case where the origin lies in ideas rather than in hormones. Somebody hears a word like "communism," "capitalism," "democracy" or "autocracy." He associates these concepts with other ideas. In his subconscious mind there has developed a fixed mental attitude with regard to their implications. He has been influenced by inflammatory speeches and biased articles which emphasize the advantage of one type of politics or economy and the disadvantages of another. His subconscious mind is also influenced by inherited xenophobia of which we have spoken before, by animal selfishness, and by innate vanity. He does not really want to think logically, because he may arrive at conclusions which conflict with his subconscious feelings. This would hurt his pride and he would feel discomfort, a sensation he tries to avoid. In order to activate the genes which communicate with the "pleasure of Cosmos" he listens with eagerness to speeches which tickle his vanity, and tries by this method to keep his mind in a state of "intoxication"; and a continuation of the process may well lead him, his followers, and innocent people as well, to war, destruction, death, and ruin.[1]

Finally we shall say a few words about *thoughts*. The power of conscious thinking is the highest faculty which has been developed among living beings on earth. It is probably the exclusive prerogative of the human race, although traces of it can be found in the higher animals. In addition to conscious reasoning there exists also a certain type of unconscious reasoning in which people think with their "feelings," and sometimes to even better advantage.

Most thinking is a conjunction of ideas and concepts. Elaborate rules have been established to secure correct deductions from premises, but most of us apply the rules without knowing or thinking about them. We have difficulty in having two ideas at the same time and the consequence is that one idea follows another in a long chain. Sensations, like images

---

[1] After this was written (in 1936) the inevitable result has appeared. A mental disease has caused a physical disaster.

or sounds (e.g. a written or a spoken word) often start this chain.

The association of ideas is interesting. The thinking organs are not confined to any particular part of the brain, probably a large portion of it acts as a unit. The immaterial structure involved does not seem to be so definitely associated with special neurones as are other mental activities. If we imagine thinking to be associated with activities of genes and genii, as is natural since the capacity of conscious thinking is inherited, the association of ideas may be an indication of a grouping of or interconnection between memory elements, such that the activation of one part causes the activation of an adjacent or connected part. Under extraordinary conditions, when the blood is surging through our veins at an abnormal speed and hormones are rushing through seldom activated parts of our brain, the association of ideas and of memories is so rapid that a connected chain of thoughts, long forgotten memories, or even our whole life history, may appear as in a flash in our consciousness. On the other hand, if we think too much about one particular thing, our thoughts are apt to wander back and forth between fixed ideas, as they often do when we are not fully awake, which we probably never are. We can become "possessed" by certain thoughts or memories, and it is necessary to break away from them by new kinds of physical or mental activities or by trying to study things from an entirely new viewpoint. Fixed ideas do not only occur among individuals; large groups of people may by often repeated written or spoken words become possessed by identical ideas to the exclusion of all others.

Thoughts, like sensations and feelings, are attributes of Cosmos. For what else can they be? *A combination of atoms can not of itself give rise to a human thought.* If we admit the cosmical nature of thoughts, we begin to realize the origin of ideas,[1] which is the same as that of the ova genes, which came to earth and determined the development of organic life as described in the preceding chapter.

We have said that thoughts can be transmitted from one individual to another (telepathy), and there is then no logical reason why they cannot be transmitted from an individual to the Soul of the Universe and from the Soul of the Universe to an individual (inspiration).

In the present chapter we tried to pass from the physical world to the mental world. On closer inspection we found them both mental, that is, they existed primarily in the consciousness of the individual. But an external world with space and time properties also existed, a world of matter and motion

[1] Many thoughts and ideas represent the reaction of our subconscious mind when stimulated by sensations and feelings. To test their value they must be compared with other data, in order to ascertain whether they are in accordance with other facts and can be incorporated into a logical system of thoughts.

governed by rules and relations and systematized in the science of physics. Of the *existence* of this world we were quite convinced, because it could be independently studied by many individuals using a great variety of methods giving consistent results. Our *description* of it, however, was of necessity incomplete and biased, since it was based exclusively on the specific properties of the space and time genes we had inherited.

We had also inherited genes for the perception of colors, sound, smell, taste, pain, heat, and cold, and the only way we could understand the existence of such mental qualities was to assume that they also had a cosmic foundation and origin. Feelings, will, and thoughts could not be conceived as accidental by-products of atomic configurations, and we were forced to assign a cosmic foundation to them as well.

The Cosmos which emerged from these considerations was of necessity a generalization of our own mental attributes. As modern science describes the external physical world as an external counterpart to or an "hypostasis" of the individual space and time perceptions, so we described the more comprehensive Cosmos as a generalization and an hypostasis of all those phenomena of which our mind is consciously aware. Man is a part of Cosmos, and the part of Cosmos of which he has the most intimate knowledge and which he can most directly study is in his own brain. There he has an inherited endowment of *living cosmic elements which have never lost their connection with their world-transcending source and origin.* With the aid of these elements man has learned much and can learn still more about certain aspects of matter, of life, of himself, and of his mind.   He can even learn a few of the secrets of the Soul of the Universe!

We are particularly interested in man, since we belong to the human race.   Before we penetrate deeper into the problem of man's ego or "soul" and its future, we shall study some special aspects of the human mind which are of particular importance for the development of the human race.

CHAPTER 10

The Development of the Human Mind

THERE ARE certain animals on the earth who have developed their minds to a much greater extent than all the others. This class of animals we call *men*. They have the same physical and mental characteristics as the higher mammals, but their power of *thinking* is so highly developed that they have succeeded in acquiring supremacy over all other animals on the earth. This intelligent animal, *Homo sapiens*, began to appear on the earth during relatively recent times, and his appearance was, at least from one point of view, the most important event in the history of the earth. There are certain reasons to believe that this new type of animal emerged at different places on the earth and at different times. Their descendents have gradually spread to different parts of the earth and can live almost anywhere. They have learned to raise their own food, to use all kinds of material for their necessities and comfort, and to transport their goods to all parts of the globe. They have invented tools, machines and instruments, studied the atoms and the stars, developed great scientific and philosophical systems, and some of them have even learned to value beauty, truth, honesty and goodness.

The development of the faculty of thinking probably went on very slowly for many thousands of years. Abstract thinking probably began with the development of language which is the necessary means for its expression. With the invention of written languages it became possible to preserve for posterity the ideas and achievements of the human race. Thanks to the use of spoken and written languages a man's knowledge is no longer limited to his personal experiences, a *collective* knowledge encompassing the experiences of a great number of individuals has become possible. When this collective knowledge has been properly systematized and freed from illusions and superstitions it becomes *science*. The *natural sciences* deal largely with space and time phenomena; analysis of the mind and of the mental processes has led to the science of *philosophy;* and the study of good and evil and of the relationship of man to Cosmos has led to *ethics* and *religion*.

Man is a *social* animal, although to a much less degree than, for instance, the bees and the termites. The natural social unit is the *family*, related families form a *tribe*, and related tribes are often called a *race*. As a rule races mix freely with one another and form societies united by common language, customs and traditions. They are then no longer racial but *cultural groups*, which sometimes are united into economic and political units called *nations*.

Although we speak about different human races, like the white, black, yellow and red, and of different types of civilization, there is much evidence for the assertion that the differences are superficial and not fundamental; they are due to environment, education and tradition and not to inherent differences. The training of Indian children in East Africa, for instance, has shown that they reach considerably higher levels in learning than the local white children.[1] The training of children in the Hawaiian Islands has shown the extraordinary similarity in mental attitude and capabilities among children of what we usually regard as greatly different races. It seems quite possible to train a few generations of races to become highly educated individuals, even though they now may be living under conditions prevalent in Europe many thousands of years ago.

If all human races have the same physical and mental capabilities, why then has the development proceeded in different directions and at quite different pace in some regions of the earth as compared with others? As organic evolution is to a large extent due to *mutations* so mental evolution seems to depend on a certain type of *variation in mental char-*

[1] Julian Huxley, Africa View, p. 216, London, 1932.

acteristics, a variation which is limited, however, to a few individuals. Such outstanding individuals think along new lines or more intensely along old lines, and if their thoughts are of direct or indirect value to the community in which they live, new habits are initiated, or new vistas of thoughts are opened for their fellowmen. Expressed in other terms, the mental development of the human race is to a large extent due to the fact that a few individuals for some reason or other have been able to establish a more intimate contact with the World Soul than the majority have succeeded in doing. If freedom of speech and of expression of new thoughts are not suppressed by the wielders of power, and, if the ignorance and the inertia of the masses are not too great, the new ideas can spread to ever widening circles. One thought leads to another, and civilization rises at an accelerated speed to ever higher levels.

Many thousands of years ago there were inspired men with mental faculties as high as any of modern times. But intellectual intercourse was not developed to any great extent, and their ideas were not or could not be submitted to any objective tests. Between two and three thousand years ago there appeared in Greece a number of sages or geniuses unsurpassed in later times. To their power of thinking mankind owes a tremendous debt.

The intellectual development of mankind is not the most important, however. In spite of his intellectual achievements man has not risen much over the animal stage. He is still a brute, and like his early ancestors he is selfish, cruel and vain. The inherited characteristics of his nature change very slowly; when the varnish of civilization is rubbed off men can revert to a stage which in many respects is below that of the animals. Not so many centuries ago men enjoyed the spectacle of seeing their enemies suffer and of seeing individuals with other beliefs than their own tortured to death. Such things can hardly occur now, but race hatred still exists and there are executions, deportations and detentions of dissenters and independent, liberty-loving spirits.

Society requires that the individuals relinquish a certain amount of freedom, and as human societies become more complex antisocial activities can not be tolerated. This fact is often used, however, to restrict the fundamental liberties of man, his freedom of thought and of worship and of expressing his opinion about his leaders and their actions. It has taken men thousands of years of development to devise safeguards to protect themselves against the usurpation by their leaders of greater power than that which has been entrusted to them by the people. Much blood has been shed and much suffering has been endured in this process, which is still going on in many countries. Like his early ancestors man is still an individualist at heart. He may temporarily be forced to give up his freedom or trade it for food, shelter and security, but his subconscious urge for development makes him sooner or later throw off his shackles and regain the freedom of his spirit which is his most valuable possession.

The rudiments of goodness probably exist in all human beings. Using the terminology in the preceding chapters we may say that the "goodness in the World Soul" has been absorbed in the germ plasm of the human race. As the optic ganglia must be stimulated by hormones before sensations of light and color can occur, and as certain nerve centers must be stimulated by chemicals like prolactin before motherly love can be realized, so goodness must be stimulated before it can become an actuality. Goodness is not a feeling, however, like pleasure and pain, happiness and sorrow, love and hate, all of which can be stimulated by chemical hormones acting on elements inherited by the human race. Goodness is a mental attitude related to *thoughts*. Like thoughts it is stimulated by ideas, and the class of ideas which are acting in this case are called *ideals*. In our consciousness we have a reflection of the cosmic ideal of goodness, and we feel, more or less regularly, an urge to imitate this ideal. The imitation is an imperfect one, but we know well what it prescribes for us all. In our selfish thoughts of gain, revenge, hate and vanity we forget the ideals. When whole nations do this we have wars and dark ages. But during the dark ages we reflect upon the futility of our previous actions, and new thoughts are born—and then the eternal light shines brighter than ever before.

The idea of goodness as the fundamental nature of Cosmos or God has been clearly realized by many thinkers. The language they use may differ and the symbolism employed may seem strange to modern men, but the ideals are fundamental and intuitive. In goodness, compassion, mercy and truth man reaches into levels of Cosmos which can not be attained by his intellect; he communicates with the very essence of the Soul of the Universe. According to Kant goodness is the result, not of theoretical, but of "practical" reason, it is a reflex of the *categorical imperative,* the unconditional command of our conscience.

Confucius and Gotama, also called Buddha, preached and practiced the spirit of goodness. Christ, who called himself the "Son of Man" and who probably had a more intimate contact with the World Soul than any other man, preached the "Sermon on the Mount," the most important contribution to the moral development of mankind. Although God for him was an inscrutable creator and a relentless judge, he was above all *Love,* and the most important command was to "love thy neighbor as thyself."

The evolution of the human mind and of ethics is an interesting chapter for the historian and the philosopher, but most of us are more interested in another problem. What is the nature of the human individual, his conscious ego or his *soul?* Does it vanish at death or live on in some form or other? Many have the idea that it does live on, but there is a feeling among modern men that the belief in the immortality of the soul may be an illusion, due to man's love of his own ego. At all events, it is thought that it can not be proved by scientific methods or even be given a reasonable, scientific basis.

When approaching this subject the reader is requested to do some courageous thinking. The thinking must not be swayed by personal feelings or by preconceived ideas. He must try to adopt a cool, detached attitude, which is very difficult, since his own destiny is in the balance. The reader must not take anything for granted, he must use his own judgment, not mine. I can only present certain facts and arguments for the reader's benefit.

We shall enter and walk along some of the very dark corridors in the foundations of Cosmos. The reader must bring his own torch along. If he does not like to enter these corridors he may stop the reading here, go to work, play, eat and sleep. But if he can think freely and is interested in his future, he is welcome to join the searching party.

CHAPTER 11

The Soul

THERE IS no doubt about the existence of the human *soul* if we define it properly. The human soul is in the first place the (ego) of the human being, a perceiving, feeling, willing, thinking and remembering entity. It is, for instance, not a set of memories, but the possessor of a particular group of memories, most of which never rise to the level of consciousness. Most men have definitely only *one* ego or personality; multiple personalities will be mentioned later.

The soul is something which gives unity to the mental complex of a man. That such a unity should be recognized and given a name was felt very early in the history of mankind. Although the "observation" of this unity is not made with the aid of our sense organs, it must, nevertheless, be regarded as valid; in fact, this observation is more direct than ordinary sense observations which only give us shadow pictures of the external world. We have become so accustomed to this unity within ourselves that it takes a mental effort to describe it in proper terms and to realize its significance.

[handwritten marginalia: The eternal, real person who owns all the attributes of mind.]

We have previously mentioned other unities in living organisms. The general and the subordinate genii have been regarded as units, which cause special genes to impart their innate structural properties to certain tissues and make possible the production of complete organs. These activities are observed with the aid of our eyes as moving shadows in our consciousness and are hence described by their structural properties in space and time. Other genii can to a certain extent be observed directly in our consciousness, the memory genie is one of them, the space-time frame, in which the elementary color sensations are incorporated and organized into a coherent unit, is another. The elements of sensations are regarded as due to "activation of sense genes." The ultimate source of elementary sensations and feelings is placed beyond the individual and in a Cosmic Consciousness, and one reason for this assumption is that mental qualities in general must have a common cosmic foundation and can not be accidental byproducts of atomic configurations. It has been pointed out that we have difficulty in thinking about different things at the same time, and we also ordinarily have only one feeling or emotion at a particular time. Our consciousness apparently has a limited capacity which gives it a unitary character at each moment of time, and our memory connects these units into a more general and permanent unit, which is the ego or the soul. Since the soul gives unity to the conscious mental activities in an individual, we may regard it as an entity of the same kind as the other genii. As the general genie of the body of an animal makes it function as a unit, so the soul, "the general genie of the mind," gives unity to its conscious activities.

Since the soul is seemingly one of the genii and its physical properties resemble in all probability those of other genii, it is of interest at this point to describe briefly the physical properties of genii in general.

A genie like a gene spirit is the source of an immaterial structure in space and time, in living organisms associated with matter. In the fertilized ovum all the genes and the genii must exist in some potential form. An egg cell can be fertilized by mechanical means (artificial parthenogenesis), hence genii can come from an ovum which has not combined with a sperm. An egg cell without a nucleus can be fertilized by a sperm, and the resultant embryo shows predominant maternal characters; if this is a general rule, it indicates that the genii in general originate in the cytoplasm of the ovum and not in the nucleus. Before the organization has taken place twins may be formed from the same ovum, or morula, hence the genii are sometimes duplicated in the first stages of embryonic development. Originally genii like genes are formed by a process of death and rebirth in the formation of germ cells. Reasons have also been given for the assertion that genii can not be annihilated, and that they can be *de novo* associated with matter.

Assuming that these properties are applicable to the soul, we find that the soul is the source of an immaterial, living structure, probably formed by splitting from a similar entity, and that it comes probably from the mother and not from the father. At a very early stage of embryonic development a soul may die, but it is immediately reborn in duplicate form in identical twins. A soul is probably not destroyed at death. Souls can also be incorporated *de novo*.

The fundamental property of a soul, as we conceive and define it, is that it retains its "identity" during the life of the individual as is shown by the existence of an unchanging memory of past events. Hence we must regard the soul as being intimately and inseparably associated with the memory genie which is known to be associated with the brain. The soul must therefore be associated with the brain, after this organ has been developed in the animal.

At the end of the last century Weismann found evidence that the cells which later develop into the reproductive organs in animals are separated from other cells at a very early stage of embryonic development. This led to the theory of the "continuity of the germ plasm," a theory accepted by many biologists, but not applicable to the plants and the lower animals which can be regenerated from almost any part. According to this theory, the "body" of an animal does not produce gametes, but is itself an outgrowth from the germ plasm. From this standpoint genii have their origin in the germ plasm of the race. Hence if a soul comes from the mother, as the genii seem to do, its immediate origin is in the maternal germ plasm of the race.

A soul in an egg cell, in an embryo, or in a new born child does not possess the qualities we ordinarily associate with this name; it is a soul in potential form only. It must receive sense impressions, accumulate memories, become a feeling, willing and thinking entity before we can say that it is actually a soul in the usual meaning of the word. At the beginning of its existence it is nothing but an empty frame or shell, a "book with blank pages," in which many things may be written, where suffering and happiness, despair and joy may be described, where pictures and incidents from childhood to old age may be recorded. Most potential souls "die" (which for living elements in general means to lose the energy necessary for interaction with space-time) before they begin to develop at all; some have a very short, others a much longer period of development. It is the "content" that is of special importance, for the frame determines only the potential capabilities of the soul. The content is not merely an accumulation of discrete mental data, there is a mysterious kind of unity or "personality" connected with it. With the acquisition of a content the soul has begun its development.

In a previous chapter evidence was given for the belief that the memory genie is extremely stable, perhaps more stable than any other immaterial, living structure. It may exist after the death of the individual, and, for all we know, it may be entirely indestructible for all "eternity." The soul is the "owner" of the memory, the personality behind it, and we have regarded it as inseparable from the memory genie. If the individual memory is indestructible and eternal, then the soul must also have these properties. There are therefore good reasons for making the following important assertion:

A soul is indestructible and immortal. As an individual it has a beginning, but seemingly no end.

The next question which arises in our mind is the following. Do animals have any souls? The higher animals have memories, they have sensations and feelings, they have affection for their masters and offspring. We can not deny them a soul of some sort. As we go down the scale of animals conscious activities become less and less prominent. The behavior of the lower animals is governed by "instincts," which correspond to our subconscious inheritance. We know nothing about the mentality of the lower animals or of plants. If we use a wide enough definition of a soul, we may say that they have souls, but very little of their mentality rises to the level of consciousness. The difference between human souls, animal souls, and plant souls—if the plants have any souls of the kind we have previously defined—seems primarily to be in the capacity of conscious activity, self contemplation, and of receiving *ideas* from the Cosmic Consciousness.

We now begin to see a possible reason why life was sent to the earth which is one of the places in the universe where organic life as we know it can exist. The idea which naturally comes to our mind is the following:

The surface of the planet Earth seems to be a place for the breeding and the incarnation of souls.

The earth is certainly a breeding place for genes. Whether or not they have any stability after death we can not yet tell, although it is a question which can be answered by definite and simple scientific tests. Organic life may well be necessary for the *splitting* of genes, genii, and potential souls, and that is perhaps why the earth must serve as a breeding place for such entities.

The most characteristic thing about the human soul after it has developed a consciousness is its remarkable individuality and integrity. We have a very definite feeling of having the same ego as we had when we were children. We feel that our memories are accumulating something which is very personal, and which never can be transferred to anyone else. We know also very well that our personality changes, much or little, quickly or slowly. An innocent boy or girl, a man or a woman, may in a few years change into entirely different personalities. There can be no doubt that the fundamental property of the human soul is that of development, combined with a retention of identity. If we accept the theory of the indestructibility of the soul, there seems to be no particular reason to assume anything contrary to this after the death of the individual. We conclude that souls probably retain their individuality for all eternity, after an individuality has once been acquired, an event which seems to take place when the general genie in the embryo begins its expansion.

Psychologists know many multiple personalities, which in some cases are entirely distinct and do not consciously know of each other's existence, although they exist in the same brain and use the same body. Trained psychologists know how to analyze such personalities, how to bring them into the full light of consciousness, and have sometimes succeeded in uniting them into a single personality. In such cases memories may perhaps have been accumulated in different "centers" of the brain. Since a multiple personality has a unitary subconscious memory, he can only have one soul.

There appears to be no great difference between the souls of the different human races now existing on the earth. Their gene complexes differ slightly, but their capabilities of receiving ideas is about the same. The state of development of the races and their aptitudes differ somewhat, but this is due to training, education, and environmental conditions. One race may have been trained along one line, whereas the training of another has gone in an entirely different direction.

Originally potential human souls with all their capabilities of development may well have been transmitted to the germ plasm of some anthropoid apes living at a certain time on the earth. We recall that a similar assumption about the origin of genes and genii was made in a previous chapter.

There have been several human races before the present. We have the Pithocanthropus from Java, the Piltdown man, the Sinanthropus, the Heidelberg man, and the Neanderthal man among the extinct races of men. Other species may have existed, but their bones have not yet been found. Then we have the Cromagnon man, quite similar to us, but also extinct. Then came the Neolithic man who possessed better training in the use of flints and more artistic ability than his predecessors. He was the ancestor of the modern man. He has probably the same kind of soul as his predecessors, but with a more completely developed system of mental genii.

The development of the mental faculties of the human race can be regarded as a gradually unfolded system of genii, just as we have regarded a new organ to be gradually "unfolded." Mental training does not create new capabilities in a race, it helps to de-

velop or unfold latent faculties. The unfoldment
is always incomplete and often one-sided, and it is
greatly influenced by the physical and mental conditions in the environment.

I do not think that the human soul has developed
from an animal soul. The capacity for abstract
thinking, for receiving and pondering over new ideas
requires probably a soul of higher type than those
in animals or plants. Since originally souls like
other things have come from or are parts of Cosmos
there is no reason to believe that the souls of all
animals are alike in their capacity for development.

The genes, the genii, and the potential souls came
originally from the World Soul and were transmitted
to the earth. Some of them found the right kind
of matter, the right temperature and environment.
From them came living organisms and men. The
absorption of the immaterial structures did not occur
at any particular time. It occurs all the time and
goes on now. New genes and genii, and perhaps
even some kind of souls with greater capabilities
than that of the present man, may appear any time
on the earth. If the absorption takes place in the
system of nerve cells, an individual with quite new
faculties might make his appearance. If it takes
place in the germ plasm, a new inheritance might
gradually or immediately be "unfolded" among his
descendants. In the latter event a new race with

superhuman powers and faculties could be produced on the earth. Any number of new mental and physical faculties, like the property of telepathic communication and the ability to fly, might in this way be acquired by the human race.

The absorption of a new genie in the germ plasm of an animal should not be regarded as an "accident." Strictly speaking nothing is accidental; if we knew *all* the factors involved, every event could be traced to precedent causes. But it must be remembered that mental events often precede and determine physical events. If we could study the activities of the subconscious mind we should probably find that biological organization is directed by a "purpose" and that all genii have some kind of "mind" and act towards a dimly conceived goal. The writer is convinced that the acquisition of a new genie depends upon the subconscious *will* of the recipient. If conditions on the earth had made flying ability a necessity for the survival of men, some individual with exceptional will power would to some extent have secured this ability for himself and in more developed form for his descendants. If we generalize this idea we come to the conclusion that an individual by great mental exertion or by an indomitable desire can open up the channels to sources in the realm beyond space and time (Cf. p. 49), sources which previously have been inaccessible to him and his race. In our own mind lies the creative power that can open the gates to this unfathomable domain in Cosmos.[1]

In the preceding we have given reasons for the belief that a soul is indestructible, and that its most characteristic property is its capabilities of development. Our next problem is therefore that of development of a soul after the death of its earthly host. While there is no direct evidence on the subject, we may throw some light on the problem by making reasonable hypotheses. Some souls have had a few years of development on earth, while others are completely blank, they are nothing but potentialities. The opportunities for development differ tremendously among different souls. If we assume that the earthly development has a *meaning*, an ulterior purpose, our inherent sense of justice tells us that it would be unfair for the different souls as individual entities to have such unequal opportunities, even if we do not consider the great waste involved in the unnecessary production of so many undevel-

[1] This idea of the origin of organization has perhaps never been more clearly expressed than by the great philosopher J. E. Boodin. In Contemporary American Philosophy, Vol. 1, page 161 (Macmillan, 1930) he writes: "My belief is that they (the types of organization) do not emerge by accident, but by virtue of the relation of our local field to the structure of the larger cosmic field and the genius of the whole.——Hence in a self-maintaining cosmos there must be a constant process of give and take. This means that *the types of organization are eternally incarnate in the cosmos, though the bearers vary and, like runners, hand over the torch of life*." (Italics by G. S.)

oped souls. Furthermore, the earthly development of most human souls is far from inspiring. The lack of opportunity from which the majority of people suffer while on earth leads to the hypothesis of a development after death. This development probably takes place in a "form" which can not be described in terms based on the present mental characteristics of the human race. Perhaps it may take the form of new earthly or planetary incarnations,[1] or in the permanent or temporary submergence of our souls in the realm beyond space and time. Many questions could be asked, but our observations tell us very little. We must have recourse to intuitions, although naturally great caution must be exercised. It is difficult to estimate the value of such "revelations," because in general they can not be subjected to unequivocal tests. But having realized the existence of a world beyond space and time where ideas

[1] Opinions differ whether human souls can be reincarnated on the earth or not. In 1936 a very interesting case was thoroughly investigated and reported by the governmental authorities in India. A girl (Shanti Devi from Delhi) could accurately describe her previous life (at Muttra, five hundred miles from Delhi) which ended about a year before her "second birth." She gave the name of her husband and child and described her home and life history. The investigating commission brought her to her former relatives, who verified all her statements. Among the people of India reincarnations are regarded as commonplace; the astonishing thing for them in this case was the great number of facts the girl remembered. This and similar cases can be regarded as additional evidence for the theory of the indestructibility of memory.

have their origin we see them in a new light. From what has been previously said it follows that revelations are possible and even probable. They are often incomplete and given in symbolic form, and not always easy of interpretation. Many so-called revelations or inspirations may well be nothing but hallucinations, comparable with the confused pictures in our dreams. On the other hand, it is very doubtful whether an entirely new idea or thought can ever *of itself* arise in a human brain.

Christ says that human souls are judged and the good go to "heaven" and the evil ones to "hell," a decision apparently valid for all eternity. But the Hebrew word *olam* and the corresponding Greek word *aion* used in this connection do not mean eternity but merely a certain time interval, which may be long or short. Christ speaks about a Divine Providence and says that "not a sparrow shall fall to the ground without the will of your Father." If we admit the existence of a loving providence it seems to us meaningless that God should permit the production of innumerable souls bound for a development which would cause eternal suffering. Christ also speaks of God as his and all other men's "Father." This intuitive conception is of special interest, since the idea has here been expressed that all the hereditary factors have originated *in complete form* in Cosmos and have gradually been unfolded on the earth. He emphasizes also the personal relationship between God and man, which idea is here expressed as a potential means of communication between the neurones in our bodies and Cosmos or the World Soul.

Swedenborg, who was well known to have very unusual clairvoyant faculties, also had visions about the conditions and developments in another world, but his symbolism is very difficult to understand; at least for the writer, who knows very little about his work. Swedenborg had also visions about a "correspondence" between life in "Heaven" and life on the earth, a correspondence which, if we recall the Cosmic origin and nature of genes and genii, seems to be the simplest explanation of our physical and mental characteristics.

At the end of this chapter we come to the important problem of *determination* and *free will* and its connection with a Divine Providence. Are events determined beforehand or can we change them by our will? To put it in a drastic form, we may ask whether or not all events in the universe, and Shakespeare's plays and Goethe's poems, and the European war with all its consequences, were predetermined in the "morning day of creation."

Practically all scientists up to twelve years ago believed that all mechanical phenomena were due to causes, acting according to definite unchangeable laws. The motion of every atom, molecule and electron was determined by its initial motion and by the electric and gravitational field in which it was moving. The field was determined by other atoms, also moving. The initial conditions were in their turn due to the conditions at a previous element of time, and so on, *ad infinitum*. The same reasoning applied not only to past events, but also to the future events in the history of the earth, the solar system and the whole universe, since all phenomena, although taking place in the most distant nebulae, have noticeable effects everywhere else.[1] We can not follow individual events, since the scale is too small for our perception, but in principle everything has a definite physical cause, determined by conditions at "the day of creation," if we presuppose such an event.

After the discovery of the Principle of Indeterminacy scientists were still convinced that all "events" in the past were definite and forever unchangeable. But for the future it was, not only in practice, but also in principle, impossible to make accurate predictions of an individual event, as, for instance, the collisions between two atoms, the emission or absorption of a photon, or the disintegration of a particular radium atom. Statistical predictions expressing the probability of a large number of events taken collectively were still possible, and the accuracy of prediction for most practical purposes was exact. Since

---

[1] A distant nebula can be photographed which means that individual atomic events at tremendous distances can have effects on matter at the earth's surface.

most of our observations cover large numbers of atoms, such predictions are all that we need, and the only ones that can be verified.

Atomic physics has hardly reached a state where it can be applied to the phenomena occurring in the human brain. The action of my will, which releases the muscular activities involved in writing a certain word, is a physical phenomenon in the sense that it is represented by space-time phenomena. Our knowledge of our own decisions, however, is not acquired by the aid of physical appliances, like microscopes, galvanometers, or x-rays, which would interfere with the functioning of the brain and make the study subject to quantum rules. The actual seat of the genie of the will is not in the atoms of the neurones, but in a living immaterial source associated with a living wave system anchored to the atoms in the neurones. The molecular structure may to some extent *reflect* the activities of the will, but it is not the *cause* of these activities. The defenders of the mechanistic determination claim, more or less explicitly, that the processes connected with activities of the will are similar to those in a non-living structure. This contention contradicts our postulate concerning the independent nature of the immaterial structure in living cells, a postulate which has been abundantly justified by the facts described in the preceding chapters. As a consequence of this postulate it seems that the will can be perfectly free, although, of course, its activities can not always be translated into physical action.

The notion that the human will has a certain degree of freedom is corroborated by the feeling we all have. We feel that we can choose between two alternatives, we can use this word or that word, we can perform a good act or an evil act, we can take life and property, but there is no definite obligation that we should do one thing rather than another.

The reason why we do certain things is very often not consciously known to us. This fact is very strikingly shown when a man in hypnotic sleep is ordered to do certain things after he has returned to a normal state. He does the things ordered, but he has often not the slightest knowledge of why he does them. As there is a subconscious thinking so there is a subconscious will, and its nature is similar to that of the instincts in animals. It is very difficult to control this subconscious will, since it is not subject to conscious reasoning. With the acquisition of conscious thinking the will of man has become partly free, more free than that of any other animal. The degree of freedom varies greatly from one individual to another. The more we are able to bring our subconscious will up into the clear light of conscious thinking, the more free we shall become, and the less we are affected by outside influences appealing to our animal feelings, in particular selfishness, revenge, and vanity.

We have said that the genes originally came from Cosmos and that they had never lost their connection with their world-transcending source and origin. When activated by hormones the "gate" to the corresponding preexisting qualities in Cosmos, for instance with "red," was opened. We have generalized this conception and applied it to feelings and even to thoughts and ideas. But how about *Will?* Are my acts which I think are due to my own free will due to an outside *Cosmic Will,* and is my sense of freedom an illusion? It is a difficult problem, our conscious logical reasoning fails us. But our subconscious mind is continuously working, and some thoughts float up to the level of consciousness and stay, others quickly disappear beneath this level. Such fragmentary thoughts have told many of us that the feeling we have of being able to deliberate and to make decisions has a profound significance, that our will is at least partly free, that God also has a will of his own, and that there is a purpose behind it all. Such fragmentary thoughts are always personal, they cannot be put in a logical form for the benefit of others. Personally I feel that God has delegated some of his power of will or decision to human souls, after they have reached a certain state of development. Only if this is the case can individual souls be in any way responsible for their acts. Punishment would be absurd and so would reward. To facilitate our choice when making decisions God has made human souls responsive to a *Cosmic Con-science*—the origin of which should be obvious to any thinking man—which rewards us with happiness for good acts and punishes us with unhappiness for intentionally evil acts. It probably also indicates the nature of "the punishment" to be expected after death. The reaction to the influence of conscience is, as we well know, quite different among different people. Certain undeveloped individuals and races and practically all animals are insensitive to its voice, whereas others are quite sensitive. Man has thus greater responsibilities than animals have, his punishment and reward are greater, and his suffering may often be a necessary part of his development.

The laws of physics which the scientists regard as unbreakable do not govern everything in the universe, as most people seem to think. The neurones in our bodies, which have made it possible for us to perceive physical phenomena and to formulate the rules which govern them, are themselves not bound by these rules. The existence of these cosmic elements in our brains has made possible the occurrence of events which physical science rules out as being completely outside the realm of finite probabilities. As a result of this violation of the probability laws of physics, we can become gods on a small scale— although we may also become devils. We have obtained intricate machines to do our work, we may behold a wonderful painting, hear a beautiful symphony, or read the expression of an inspiring thought. The machines, the paintings, the printed notes or letters, are atomic configurations which are incompatible with the laws of chance on which modern physics is founded—they are governed by a *purpose*. If we had a wider vision, perhaps the Cosmic Will would also appear as being governed by a purpose. There are reasons to believe that the chance that seems to rule the world is only apparent and due to the fact that our inherited mental faculties give us a cognition of the world in the form of incomplete and apparently unrelated "perspectives," which do not bring out the causal connections between the events in Cosmos.

From this viewpoint events on earth, like accidents, death, wars, our attitude toward life and toward our fellowmen, are partly due to a Cosmic Will and partly to my will and that of my fellowmen. The development of the human race on earth is conditioned by a Cosmic Will, partly by direct action (physical laws) and partly by indirect or delegated action (effects of the human will). Providence often determines conditions, environment, life and death; human will determines the special development of its owner's soul under the given conditions—for some of which he cannot in any way be regarded as responsible.

We begin to see the meaning of many things which have happened on the earth. As we follow the history of the human race on earth, we see how man must learn by painful experience, we see how edifying lessons are given, how selfishness leads to destruction, how cruelty to men and animals is punished by suffering, how vanity is held up to ridicule, how hate begets hate, how the poison of envy and jealousy destroys happiness, and how greed leads to avarice. We see how charity, tolerance, and peacefulness [1] are rewarded by longevity, happiness, and beautiful mental development. Sometimes they are rewarded by death from cruel hands, but the profit to the individual is indestructible, since the development goes on for all eternity. We see how a kind word of understanding gives better and more lasting results than can be obtained with fists or guns, at least in the case of peoples or individuals who can hear the voice of conscience. At perhaps no time in human history have the lessons been so evident, their purpose so clear, as at the present time.

---

[1] Tolerance and peacefulness imply the least possible interference with the free development of individuals. Conversely, outside pressure upon or restraint of an individual's free development can not be tolerated beyond a certain degree. Defense against such influence is morally justified, but there are in general more effective means than those recorded in the history of the human race. In the end the score is always settled by a higher power than man.

"Though the mills of God grind slowly, yet they
grind exceeding' small;
Though with patience He stands waiting, with exact-
ness grinds He all."

(Friedrich von Logan, translated by Longfellow).

CHAPTER 12

Retrospection

W E HAVE come to the end of our journey. In a boyish spirit and with flying colors we set out on a new kind of adventurous exploration, caring little about the jeers from the people playing on the shore or the polite smiles of learned men. We visited the places we heard of in school, we looked at railroad trains and swinging pendulums, at atoms and cells, plants and animals, we gazed out into cosmic space and into our own minds. In inorganic substances we found material elements surrounded by wave systems, and in living matter we found, in addition, immaterial elements from which complex wave systems emerged into the domain of space and time to disappear again at death. The material and the immaterial elements were found to be sources connecting the world of space and time with the world of life and consciousness. The more complex sources we called genii, and they directed the growth and activities of living organisms. We saw animals and plants as complex structures of living elements, and we thought we could regard these elements as tones in a cosmic symphony vibrating throughout space and animating the matter at the earth's surface. We saw the life on the earth change from single cells to the familiar plants and animals. As the cosmic drama was unfolded we had a look behind the curtain and recognized the meaning of death.

Then we tried to explore the mind and found it in constant communication with Cosmos. Genii were again at work, building up pictures and memories in our consciousness, and we imagined we saw the origin of feelings, of thoughts, and of ideas.

We studied the remarkable development of men's power of thinking; we saw how he had learned to value beauty, truth, honesty and goodness. We found that the spirit of unselfishness had been carried to the earth and had begun its long fight against the animal instincts.

Then we went deep down into dark regions of our own consciousness. We met a new genie, the soul, but he was really an old acquaintance whom we often had met when we contemplated ourselves.

We found then that the soul, like some other genii, had a beginning, but no end. Its experiences were written in a script, which the ravages of time could not delete. We realized the great power of the human will, but we saw also at work a Cosmic Will. We found that man had begun to develop a new organ, sensitive to the voice of a Cosmic Conscience. His will had become more free than that of the animals, and with the freedom had come responsibilities and new possibilities of development.

People in the places we visited spoke about a God as the creator and director of the universe. Naturally we became interested, since we had set out on a search for something of the same sort. In many cases their notions were primitive, their ideas having developed partly from a fear of the unknown and from a desire for protection. In other cases their notions had originated from the intuitive feelings of inspired men, whose contact with the World Soul was more intimate than that of their fellow men.

With regard to the universe as a whole we were like ants in a great factory trying to understand why the wheels were turning and to grasp the meaning and use of the finished products. Perhaps we were conceited when we first thought that the factory had something to do with our own existence and destiny, but when we found that *we* apparently had faculties of a higher type than those possessed by all the stars and star systems the factory had produced, we realized that we ourselves might well be very important, but unfinished products, in spite of our present shortcomings and our extreme smallness. We raised our heads, a thrill went through our hearts; for we had found that our spirits were free and eternal like God himself.

During our travels we have come very far from where we started. But there is no turning back in this kind of journey. On and on we must sail through eternity, learning new lessons and performing new missions, all the time preparing ourselves for bigger and bigger tasks in the service of the *Inscrutable One*.

This seems to be our Destiny.

> Creation rejoices and sings
> In tune with a Cosmic plan,
> Nature eternally brings
> Wonders in stars and man.
> The eagle in the summer sky,
> The worm beneath the sod,
> The sun, the moon, and you, and I,
> We live and move in God.
>
> Sister Benediction

Index